Best of British
BOTTLED
BEER

CONTENTS:

First published 1995

ISBN 0 7110 2298 4

Published by Dial House

an imprint of Ian Allan Ltd, Terminal House, Station Approach, Shepperton, Surrey TW17 8AS.
Printed by Ian Allan Printing Ltd, Coombelands House, Coombelands Lane, Addlestone, Weybridge, Surrey KT15 1HY.

Photographs by the author and breweries except those supplied by Food Features on pages:5, 6-7, 15, 29L, 29R, 30R, 30L, 30B, 31L, 32, 35L, 36, 39, 41L, 47, 50L, 54TR, 54TL, 58, 72, 78, 83, 86.

The bottled beer scene is continually changing—the details of the products described herein were correct as far as could be ascertained in 1994.

Best of British
BOTTLED
BEER

Hugh Madgin

**DIAL
HOUSE**

Introduction

Ever since the early 1970s, public awareness of the different types and brands of beers available in the UK has grown enormously. This is as much the result of the Campaign for Real Ale, launched to focus and direct the reaction of the discerning drinker against the seemingly relentless shift to an ever-shrinking number of bland keg beers, as the effect of the heavy advertising which has always been a part of the brewing industry. The days when a customer would be confronted with a bank of naked handpumps in a bar and would simply ask for 'mild', 'bitter', 'best' or 'old', are long past, and pumpclips have for years now indicated just which draught beers are on offer.

The 'Breweries' section in the *Good Beer Guide* has for a long time now provided an invaluable reference for the real draught beers on sale across the country, and there are many who spend their time seeking out every brew listed therein. Information on the bottled beers to be found across the country is less easy to come by. Hidden on shelves often at floor level behind the bar in the pub, and under sustained pressure from canned beer in the off-trade, bottled beers are often overlooked and have suffered a marked decline in popularity which has only very recently begun to be reversed. This small guide attempts to chart what is currently on offer, listing, by alphabetical order of each brewer, **every** bottled beer currently produced in the UK.

The majority of bottled beers are, of course, not 'real', in the sense that they have been filtered and pasteurised, to ensure clarity and longer shelf life. This means that the subtle complexities of taste in a living beer undergoing secondary fermentation in the cask are mostly not present, but where real draught beers can vary from excellent to undrinkable, depending on the skill with which they are kept, one is guaranteed consistency with pasteurised beer in the bottle, one of the reasons for the rise of bottled beer in the first place. Although, it must be said that many bottled beers suffer in pubs from being kept on cold shelves which chill away most of the flavour.

Every British brewer has been contacted in the compilation of this guide, and while some have proved frustratingly coy at revealing their bottled products (one major East Anglian regional was reluctant to give details on all but three of its bottled beers, its marketing department saying of the others 'we don't like to push those'), it is thought that every bottled beer regularly brewed in the UK has been included. It is inevitable that during the delay between compilation and publication events will overtake some of the entries recorded here, and any corrections and updates sent via the publisher will be most gratefully received for possible future editions.

The beers listed range in annual production figures from those measured in millions to just 30 dozen bottles. No attempt has been made to give qualitative judgements of the beers listed; the beers mentioned herein vary, in the opinion of the compiler, from the insipid to the truly great, but as such opinions are necessarily subjective, the best thing is for the reader to go and taste them for him or herself.

Hugh Madgin
Stevenage

The Background

180ml

EXCEPTIONALLY STRONG

BANKS'S OLD ALE

BREWED TO AN ORIGINAL
GRAVITY BETWEEN
1094°-1102°

BARLEY WINE

Alc. 9.1% by vol.

BEST BEFORE END** DATE: SEE LABEL EDGE

JAN | FEB | MAR | APR | MAY | JUN | JLY | AUG | SEP | OCT | NOV | DEC | 1991 | 1992 | 1993

BREWED AND BOTTLED BY
THE WOLVERHAMPTON & DUDLEY BREWERIES, PLC
WOLVERHAMPTON ENGLAND.

O riginally, when beer first began to be bottled, the act of bottling it was simply that of putting it in bottle rather than cask. Every bottled beer was as 'live' as the draught beer, but was simply more portable. The secondary fermentation continued, and, depending on the strength of the brew, it would mature over months or even years. Such beers are described as bottle-conditioned, and until the late 19th century all bottled beers were so. The desire for consistency and a clarity (a live beer inevitably has a small amount of sediment at the bottom of the bottle) led to beer for the bottle being chilled, to precipitate out solids, then filtered, to remove the solids, before being pasteurised to kill any remaining yeast in the beer. Carbon dioxide would also be added to give the beer its sparkle in place of that which would be produced naturally by secondary fermentation. The marketing of bottled beers in the early part of the 20th century made great play of the brightness of the lighter beers, and many pale and light ales had the sobriquet 'Crystal', a term which has not (quite) died out. In many ways the explosion of popularity experienced by bottled beers in the period from World War 1 to the 1950s, was the precursor of the rise of 'kegged' beer somewhat later. The product was more predictable, which (and this may be heresy to a generation which suffered the worst excesses of keg blandness during the 1960s and early 1970s) was a strong selling point to drinkers, and above all, could be taken home in the smallest of quantities and left in the larder for months if need be without

deteriorating. For the brewers, the development of mechanised bottling lines from the latter half of the 19th century also made bottled beer more economic.

Although increasingly in the minority, bottle-conditioned brews remained. From the major breweries Bass Red Triangle and Worthington White Shield, as well as Barclay Perkins (latterly Courage) Imperial Russian

Stout and Guinness continued to be live in the bottle for many years, as did a dwindling number of beers from the smaller brewers, such as Gale's Prize Old Ale. The revival of interest

in bottled brews has seen a resurgence in the number of bottle-conditioned beers in the last few years, and happily three of the five mentioned above are still with us, although, ironically, just as bottle-conditioned beers started to make a comeback, Guinness ceased in 1993 to sell its bottled Original as a live beer,

citing the nine-month shelf life of pasteurised Original, compared with three for the 'original' Original.

There are said to be as many as 30 different types of British beer, although hard and fast distinctions are difficult to make; for example the difference between a pale and light ale is very difficult to pin down.

A summary of the main types of bottled beer brewed in Britain is given below:

Brown Ale: Dark in colour, this is the bottled equivalent of draught dark mild. Brown ales tend to be sweet, but a drier form using roasted malt was popular in the bottle and known as Burton ale. Burton browns were usually stronger than sweet brown ales, but the sole survivor of this genre, Greene King Burton, is the same strength as that brewery's sweet brown ale. Brown ales are often branded 'Nut Brown' due to their 'nutty' taste.

may well be stronger than another's pale ale, and so the distinction between the two tends to blur. Family, Dinner and Luncheon ales were common at one time as terms for the weakest of light ales; now the only survivor of this custom is Scottish & Newcastle's Home Luncheon.

Whereas Family and Dinner ales have vanished from the brewer's lexicography, the term India Pale Ale, which

Pale Ale: Pale ales are by definition dry and highly hopped, being the bottled equivalent of bitter. Indeed a number of bottled pale ales, such as Bathams, Crown Buckley and Scottish & Newcastle's Theakstons are marketed as Bitter.

There are variations within the broad classification 'pale ale'. Light ale (referring to the alcoholic strength, not the colour) is the term for the weaker pale ales and light ales tend to be more lightly-hopped than pale ales, and more sweet in taste. Many breweries used to brew both a light and a pale ale, Whitbread continuing to offer the two varieties to this day. However, one brewery's light ale

had nearly vanished by the 1970s, has had a resurgence, both for draught bitter and bottled pale ale as the real ale revival has taken hold. Originally used to describe stronger pale ales exported to India, the term is often abbreviated to IPA.

Stronger pale ales are Special and Export beers such as Courage Bulldog or Fullers ESB Export.

Stout: A high degree of roasted malts gives stout its distinctive dark taste and dark colour. Highly dried, malts with strong flavour are used to brew stout, the name for this type

of beer being reputed to be derived from Henry Stout, a Hertford brewer of the late 17th century. Stout can be so dark in colour that the froth at the top of a glass when it is poured out can be brown rather than white, which is invariably the case with other dark beers. There are two types of stout: the smooth, sweet variety and the dry. The former used to often be termed milk stout to emphasise its smoothness until the Trades Descriptions Act of 1968 outlawed this as the beer of course contained no milk and today the only brewer in the British Isles to use this term is the Guernsey Brewery. The 1968 Act does not apply on Guernsey. Sweet stout was one of the beer types to grow in popularity in parallel with sales of bottled beers in the 1930s, but in the last 20 years or so there has been a marked fall-off in demand for

bottled stout. Few are the independent brewers which have persisted with their own bottled stout, for as well as the market for sweet stout declining, national brands such as Jubilee (Bass) and above all Mackeson Stout (Whitbread) have mopped up what remains. In Scotland there is considerable demand for very sweet stouts of extremely low alcohol content.

Dry stout has been dominated by Guinness for very many years, and with the cessation of the brewing of draught Guinness after World War 2 there were, until the introduction of keg draught Guinness, two decades when stout could truly be said to survive only as a bottled beer. The last 10 years have seen the introduction of a number of new keg stouts to claim some of the market which Guinness has had to itself for so long, and very recently, cask conditioned draught stout and new bottled stouts have been introduced by independent brewers.

Porter: If stout had disappeared as a draught beer by the 1960s, Porter had, except in Ireland, vanished completely. Its name reputed to derive from its popularity with market porters in London in the 18th century, when its dominance of the beer market was unchallenged, Porter suffered from the shift towards pale ales from the

mid-19th century and had virtually died out by 1920. Midway in consistency between pale ale and stout, Porter is

can be of more than 10% alcohol by volume. As in the case of sweet stout, a Whitbread product, Gold Label barley wine, has in recent years swept many other barley wines into oblivion.

Lager: Often thought of as a comparatively recent innovation, lager was actually first brewed in the UK back in 1882. Meeting little acceptance until the 1930s, this pale beer style,

喜 壽

黄山啤酒
Yellow Mountain BEER

30ml

ABV 4.5%

適

...WED AND BOTTLED BY THE WEST COAST BREWING CO. LTD.

THIS IS

Black Sheep A

The culmination of five generations of brewing expe Brewed at Paul Theakston's Black Brewery in Masham, North Yo And nowhere else.

dark in colour and tends to be of middle to high gravity, such as Nethergate's Old Growler which has an alcohol content of 5.5% by volume. Ten years after the heights (or depths?) of the lager revolution it is remarkable to see Porter on sale in supermarkets throughout the country.

Barley Wine: Matured for a very long period, up to 18 months in some cases, barley wine is the strongest of all the mainstream bottled beer styles. Usually sold in nip (⅓pt) size bottles, barley wines

which is bottom-fermented unlike other types of beer in the UK, has enjoyed enormous popularity, and, although this is now beginning to wane, Britain's best-selling beer at the time of writing was the keg version of Carling Black Label, a beer of Canadian origin, brewed, and bottled, by Bass. The term lager is derived from the German word meaning 'to store', and it is indeed stored to mature, for as much as a year in some cases. Lager is usually served cold.

Every type of British beer has been bottled, from the weakest light ale to the heaviest barley wine. Indeed, Britain's strongest beer, Eldridge Pope's Thomas Hardy's Ale, is a bottle-conditioned brew which will mature in the bottle to

exclusively) due to the enterprise of the new micro-brewers. Once-universal terms long vanished from the draught beer portfolio such as Dinner or Luncheon ale for weaker light ales and Stingo for strong ale survived for years in bottled form, although there is now only Scottish & Newcastle's Home Luncheon Ale to

BLACK SHEEP ALE

THE BLACK SHEEP BREWERY PLC
MASHAM, YORKSHIRE HG4 4EN

ALC. 4.4% VOL. SERVE COOL

500ml ℮

BEST BEFORE END

L				JAN	FEB	MAR	APR	MAY	JUN	JUL	AUG	SEP	OCT	NOV	DEC	94	95	96
1	2	3	4															

perfection after 10 years and is perfectly drinkable for 25. By virtue of the fact that small quantities can be brewed intermittently due to the longer shelf life of bottled beer compared to draught, types of beer which vanished in draught form virtually completely, such as sweet stout, have survived for many years in bottled form, although happily a good variety of draught stouts is reappearing, mainly (but not

represent the former, and both Higson's and Watney's Stingos have comparatively recently ceased production.

Just as the English language continually evolves, so does taste in beer, although the latter has not always been consumer-led as in the case of the move towards weaker beers during and after World War 1, and the keg and lager revolutions in the last 30 years have shown. The number of bottled beers brewed in the UK has declined enormously in the last few decades,

partly due to the massive reduction in the number of breweries, the emergence of heavily-promoted national brands such as Mackeson stout and Gold Label barley wine, which so many of the remaining independent breweries have chosen to sell rather than their own brand, and partly because demand for beer types such as brown ale has simply declined in favour of other types of drink. Frank Baillie's *Beer Drinker's Companion* in 1974 mentions 499 different bottled beers brewed in the UK, the total having dropped by more than a hundred since then, despite the introduction of many new brews from the new micro-breweries.

However, just as the 1970s saw a revival of interest in, and availability of, cask-conditioned beer, mainly in the form of bitter, as the 1980s wore on, increasing attention was paid to dark beers, first in the form of mild which had effectively died out in many parts of the country. This then spread to other dark beers such as stout and porter, and now, sparked undoubtedly and ironically in part by the fashion for 'designer' bottles of imported lager at the end of the 1980s, bottled beer is once again becoming a growth area.

The way is currently being led by recently-founded micro-breweries, set up usually to brew cask beers, but which are finding that there is a ready market for their beers in bottle, whether bottle-conditioned or not. Supermarket chains have been quick to offer quality British bottled beers, where once only canned and PET bottles were available, and for Christmas 1993 the Safeway chain launched a pack of 10 British bottles entitled the 'Best of British'. Early in 1994 bottled beer made a reappearance in InterCity buffet cars, with Holsten Pils and Grolsch lager putting an end to many years of 'cans only' on trains. The major national

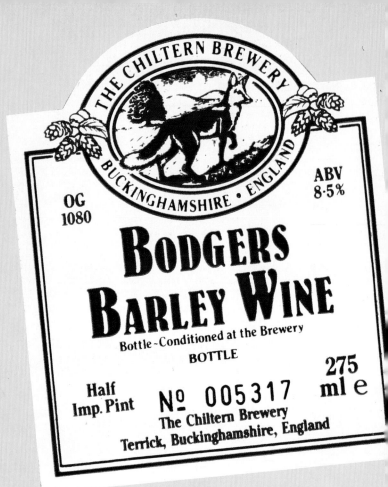

THE CHILTERN BREWERY

BUCKINGHAMSHIRE • ENGLAND

OG
1080

ABV
8·5%

BODGERS
BARLEY WINE

Bottle-Conditioned at the Brewery

BOTTLE

Half
Imp. Pint

N⁰ 005317

275
ml e

The Chiltern Brewery
Terrick, Buckinghamshire, England

breweries have caught on rapidly, with Worthington White Shield being relaunched and new premium beers such as Distinction and Black Dove being launched by Bass for example, but revival of interest in bottled beer has come just too late for many stalwarts. As some brewers expand their ranges of brewery-conditioned and bottle-conditioned bottled beers, many breweries are still jettisoning their bottled products. Some, such as Hardys & Hansons which ceased to bottle its beers in 1993, have moved to producing canned beers, while others such as Brains of Cardiff have recently cut back their range of bottled products from half a dozen to just the one example.

However, when low-alcohol beers

and lagers are taken into account, the number of bottled beers at 422 has stabilised, and indeed has risen slightly compared with the late 1980s. The darkest days for bottled beer appear to have passed; a perhaps surprising variety of long-established bottled beers remains, and the prospects for consolidation and diversification into new and revived brews at last look bright.

The Bottles

The first bottled beers appeared in the 17th century, the bottles being of a spherical shape with a long neck, after the style of the contemporary wine bottles. A cork was used to close the bottle, this being wired to ensure that it did not come loose. Records exist of beer being shipped abroad in bottles from the beginning of the 18th century, but difficulties with ensuring that the cork kept an airtight seal, and the level of taxation on glass made bottled beer a comparative rarity until the 19th century. By the 1820s, squat-shaped bottles were being produced for the carriage of beer, these being made in three parts under a process invented by Henry Ricketts of Bristol. Previously, the capacity of the bottle was determined by the glass blower, and it was only the blower's skill that made large numbers of bottles have roughly the same capacity. At this time, the bottle continued to be closed by corks. Taxes on glass continued until 1845, and it was only after then that it became economic to place beer (relatively cheap then, as now, in comparison with wine) into glass bottles. Refinements to the bottle manufacturing process took place,

with the three-part mould used by the Ricketts process giving way to a two-part mould. Bottles of beer with paper labels began to be mass produced from around the middle of the 19th century, and wired-on corks were supplanted by metal clamps holding both corks and stone stoppers, until in 1872 the internal thread screw stopper was patented by Henry Barrett. While swing-top ceramic bungs complete with rubber seals (as revived by Grolsch and Newquay Steam Beer in recent years), provided an alternative but expensive form of bottle closure, the chunky black stopper with a rubber seal screwed into the neck of the bottle remained the standard for many years. The Crown cap (the circular piece of metal crimped over the top of the neck) was introduced from the USA to the UK soon after 1910, and became universal by the 1960s. Bottle sizes have always been pretty standard; the quart flagon, pint, split or half pint, and nip or third of a pint being the norm.

The Trades Descriptions Act of 1968 led to bottles having to display the volume of their contents on the label, this was standardised as just below the 6²⁄₃oz, 10oz and 20oz of the nip, half pint and pint, a minimum contents being displayed so that fluctuations slightly below the round figure were not a contravention of the law. The flagon was very popular in the 19th century (before World War 1 pub customers commonly used quart glasses), and a few years ago, a handful of brewers still used such bottles. At the time of writing, the only brewer still to supply its beer in quart flagons is Crown Buckley in South Wales, and then only for one beer. The 'reputed quart' bottle of 26⅔oz has in recent years followed the 'reputed pint' of 13⅓oz into oblivion, although the latter has been revived by the Heritage Brewery for its Thomas Sykes Ales. Nip size bottles have generally only been used for the very strongest beers. Apart from one or two exceptions, such as the old-style bottles used for Gale's Prize Old Ale, by the 1970s all beer bottles conformed to a standard design for each size, known as the London Standard. This was adopted in the 1950s to provide complete interchangeability between breweries, and thus a London Standard bottle in a form of 'longshore drift' could conceivably in the course of its lifespan be refilled at every bottling plant in the country. Bottles can have a very long life; even today ancient half pint bottles which are the same height as the London Standard design can occasionally appear in a crate – the compiler has found two from breweries which ceased to exist more than 30 years ago in his local, their embossed lettering largely worn away by countless trips to bottling plants, but still decipherable.

With some notable exceptions, such as a number of the bottled beers of Samuel Smith and Scottish & Newcastle, beer bottles are universally brown in colour, the degree of darkness being caused by the amount of iron added in the glassworks. Green bottles for beer were once very common, lasting until well after World War 2, but brown or 'amber' is now ubiquitous. The colouration of beer bottles results from the fact that beer is sensitive to light and prolonged exposure to bright light will affect the flavour and aroma of the beer adversely.

The bottle itself has become an integral part of the identity of bottled beer brands in recent years, and a wide variety of non-standard designs are now proliferating for beers purchased in the off-trade (supermarkets and off-licences) which are generally non-returnable. So important is the design of the bottle in the marketing of the beer it contains, that in 1994 the brewer Shepherd Neame made a successful High Court action against Ushers as it felt that a square-shouldered half-litre design used by Ushers was a plagiarism of the type of bottle used for Shepherd Neame's Bishop's Finger beer. Greene King, having launched a 'designer' bottle for its Abbot Ale in the off-trade, continues to put the beer in London Standards for its pubs.

Although their design and method of closure may have changed over the years, beer bottles remained uniform in that they were returnable, with a deposit payable, and their sizes were invariably of the standard capacities listed above. This has changed significantly since the 1960s, due to two factors. First, the change away from the screw stopper to the crown cap and reductions in the weight and cost of the glass bottles has made it less imperative that they be returned to the brewery for further use. Changes in the off-trade with the advent of licences for supermarkets which are not geared to take back bottles for return to the brewery and a general shift to disposable packaging led to the one-trip or NRB (non-returnable bottle) being adopted in the UK to a far greater extent than in Europe or America. This has been accompanied by the development of the PET (poly-ethylene-terephthalate) plastic bottle for the larger sizes, which are also non-returnable. With the pattern for take-home beer being largely set by canned beers, the proportion of bottles returned to off-licences for repeated use is a tiny fraction of what it was 20 years ago. Sadly the environmental implications of the millions of plastic and NRB glass bottles bulldozed into landfill sites every week appear to be unheeded. While returnable bottles are now the exception in the off-trade, the vast majority of bottles in the on-trade continue to be reused, although many of the Pils-style bottles used for a large number of lagers in pubs are not returnable.

The second major change to the type of bottle used is the result of metrication. The few standard sizes have been supplanted by 'Euro' sizes (usually denoted by an 'e' on the bottle label). Thus sizes of 33cl (330ml), 50cl (500ml) and a litre have become common, especially for NRBs. European Community regulations have since the 1970s insisted that the metric equivalents of the imperial size be given on bottle labels, and so the $6^{2}/_{3}$oz, $9^{2}/_{3}$oz and $19^{2}/_{3}$oz of the nip, half pint and pint have become 180ml, 275ml and 550ml respectively. As they are more recognisable to the majority of drinkers, and are set to remain the norm in pubs, bottle sizes are referred to in the listing of this guide in their imperial form, except where a metric-sized bottle is used, its size then being shown as a fraction of a litre.

Societies

There are two societies which cater for the bottled beer enthusiast. The Association of Bottled Beer Collectors covers the subject with an emphasis on one-off commemorative brews and has five meetings a year. A bi-monthly magazine *What's Bottling* is produced, and membership costs £5 per annum. Further details (with SAE please) from Mike Peterson, 127 Victoria Park Road, Tunstall, Stoke-on-Trent ST6 6DY. The other organisation, the Labologists Society, is introduced by Jim Gartside below.

The Labologists

Greetings, fellow beer enthusiast. Since you have enough interest in bottled beers to read this book, you may not be surprised to learn that there are many others out there who share your interest. The Labologists Society is a diverse group of people who share at least one thing in common: a keen appreciation not only of the beers produced by the nation's brewers, but also of the attractive and varied labels designed to draw your eye towards the brewer's product on its shelf in the pub or supermarket. The Society includes collectors of all kinds of labels, but in practice, most of its members collect beer bottle labels.

Our 350 members have given many reasons for collecting beer labels. The reason I like best is 'If you collect stamps you can go to a Post Office, but if you collect beer labels, you can go to a pub!' In my own case, I was fond of travelling around Britain by rail, and got into the habit of bringing back obscure strong ales to use as aperitifs before the Sunday dinner. Wanting to keep a memento of some pleasant outings, I removed the labels, waited until I had a few dozen, and mounted them in a frame as an ornament, with the approval of the 'other half'.

What was to amaze me later was the world of brewery history, illustrated by labels going back to Victorian times, that opened up when I joined the Society after reading a newspaper article explaining that many other people did the same sort of thing. However, I am jumping ahead, and I want to mention a more unusual reason for collecting labels in times gone by. During World War 1, servicemen travelled around the country to various establishments and for reasons of security were not allowed to keep diaries. One way to record their travels was to keep albums of labels removed from beer bottles, and as breweries were mainly small local affairs in those days, the locations could be recorded quite precisely and the collections could be quite large.

To return to the historical aspect of the hobby, it is surprising how many brewing companies existed even as late as the 1960s. Many of these have become consolidated by merger and takeover into the few national combines that we have today. It is sometimes possible to track a national brand back through a series of takeovers, to a product of a local brewery earlier this century, to see how the emblems on the label have retained their characteristics after new companies have added their own style, and to wonder why this particular beer was retained when so many others disappeared.

Having got an interest in brewery history through labels, it is possible to travel around and see old breweries now used for other purposes. These include modern offices, an arts centre, housing, a riding school, industrial units, and in several cases a new micro-brewery rising from the ruins of the old concern. In the old days, label collectors might find dusty or mildewed boxes full of old labels left in attics of disused buildings, but the attics are now all cleared out and those days are sadly gone. However, a visit to admire an old country brewery is a good excuse for a day out especially if you find a nearby pub that may have sold that brewery's Josiah Fossick's Old Threshers' Strong Ale once upon a time (if you let your imagination go a bit).

Within the Society there is an exchange system for labels, old and new, and members are happy to swap like for like in order to build up their collections. This is often done by post, though meetings are frequently publicised for members to get together and swap labels and chat over a few pints. The Society organises a number of brewery trips for members and friends all over the country, one recent event being a weekend tour of the breweries around Alloa. Some people join mainly for the trips, some for the social aspect, some because they collect other forms of breweriana like pumpclips, but the main activity overall is the acquisition, exchange and discussion of the vast number and variety of labels that have been issued since the first known example in 1843. Many collectors specialise in labels from a particular area, for instance their home county, city or town. Guinness labels are a particular favourite and there is a wide variety of these, including examples for export all over the world. One of the early examples in my own collection carries an endorsement from the Royal College of Surgeons in Dublin, extolling the purity of the product and describing it in glowing terms as 'food as well as a stimulant and tonic'. These days you are more likely to find a government health warning. Commemorative labels are popular with many, including the very collectable Royal Ales, special limited-edition brews, and unusual local events such as the 1,000th (yes, really) Anniversary of Hatherleigh Bowling Club.

The Labologists Society was first formed in 1958, sponsored by Guinness as part of the activities marking its own 200th anniversary. We were left to stand on our own feet a year or so later, and have survived to become a healthy international organisation with members in North America, the Far East and Australasia as well as most European countries. Few founder members remain, but some of those who were fortunate to have been around in the early days have amassed collections of more than 40,000 labels including beautiful period pieces from Victorian and Edwardian times.

The Society prides itself on the good relations it has built up with brewers over the years. Since 1983 we have held an annual Label of the Year competition with the aim of encouraging excellence in new label design. The presentation of the awards has been held at a different brewery every year and this event has become the high spot in our calendar. We appreciate that the hobby is one which relies on the goodwill of breweries to feed our collections, and in order to give something back, we organise fund raising each year with the proceeds going to a charity nominated by the host brewery. At the last event, which was generously hosted by Arkell's in Swindon, we were delighted to raise more than £2,200 for a local hospice to show our thanks to the brewing industry for its support of our hobby.

I hope you have found this brief article interesting, and perhaps you may consider joining us. If so, I will be happy to send full details of membership if you write to me at 51 Grove Avenue, London W7 3ES. Cheers!

Jim Gartside

The Listing

The bottled beers brewed in the UK for sale in the domestic market are arranged by brewery, the brewers with bottled beers in their portfolio being listed alphabetically. Beers are listed in order of alcohol by volume (except for some produced on Guernsey where this is not recorded, the original gravity being the bench mark there), with 'NABLABs' (no-alcohol/low-alcohol beers) being listed last. In Scotland, beers have long been grouped by the historic sum of duty payable on a barrel (36gal). Thus 60/– denotes the weaker band, corresponding with light and brown ale, 70/- the pale ale/best bitter strengths and 80/- and 90/- the strong pale ale/barley wine end of the range.

The name of each brand is shown in the left hand column, with its alcohol by volume, followed by the size(s) of bottle in which the beer is sold and the date when first sold in bottle. The latter point is shown where possible; in many cases, the date of origin is no longer recorded by the brewery.

Abington

Abington Brewery
Havelock Street
Bedford
MK40 4LU
(see **Charles Wells**)

Adnams

Adnams & Company PLC
Sole Bay Brewery
Southwold
Suffolk
IP18 6JW

A small regional brewer for most of its career, the firm of Adnams became more widely known in the 1970s when it expanded its activities in the free trade market considerably. Broadside is found away from Adnams' main trading area and was initially brewed to commemorate the 300th anniversary of the Battle of Sole Bay, fought off the Suffolk coast.

Champion Pale Ale
ABV 3.1%	½pt	early 20th century

Nut Brown
ABV 3.2%	½pt	early 20th century

Broadside
ABV 4.5%	½pt	1972

Suffolk Strong Ale
ABV 4.5%	2litresPET	1988

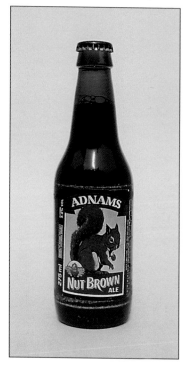

Alloa (see **Carlsberg-Tetley**)

Ann Street
Ann Street Brewery
Ann Street
St Helier
Jersey
JE1 1BZ

Founded in 1890, the brewery is now the only one left on Jersey. Its competitor Randalls Vautier (not to be confused with Randalls of Guernsey) is now simply a pub-owning group.

Mary Ann Pale Ale
ABV 3.6%   ½pt & 1pt   1930s
Mary Ann Brown Ale
ABV 3.6%   ½pt & 1pt   1930s
Mary Ann Special
ABV 4.5%   ½pt   1968
Mary Ann Jubilee Pils
ABV 7%   ⅓ litre   1977

Arkells
Arkells Brewery Ltd
Kingsdown
Swindon
Wilts
SN2 6RU

This family-owned and -run brewery celebrated 150 years of brewing in 1993, having moved to its present site in 1861.

3Bs
ABV 4.0%   ½pt   1960s

Aston Manor
Aston Manor Brewery Co Limited
Thimble Mill Lane
Aston
Birmingham
B7 5HS

Set up in 1983, the vast majority of the

Aston Manor Brewery's output is for the take-home trade.

Aston Manor Bitter
ABV 3.0%   ½ litre NRB,
                 2 & 3 litre PET   1983
Aston Manor Mild
ABV 3.0%   2 & 3 litre PET 1983

Atlas
Preston Brewing Co Ltd
Atlas Foundry Estate
Brieryfield Road
Preston
PR1 8SR

Founded in 1992, the Preston Brewing Co has adopted as its brand name and trade mark the name of the former foundry from which it operates.

Atlas Really Strong Export
ABV 6.5%   ½litre   1994

Ballards
Ballards Brewery Ltd
Unit C
The Old Sawmill
Nyewood
Rogate
Petersfield
Hampshire
GU31 5HA

This brewery, which dates from 1980, produces a bottled beer each year, whose original gravity matches the date. Each brew differs slightly from the one before and the 1992 and 1993 brews are available at the time of writing. The beers are bottle-conditioned and each bottle is numbered.

Old Episscopal
9.4 ABV   ½pt   1992

Cunning Stunts
ABV9.5%   ½pt   1993

Banks's Hansons

The Wolverhampton & Dudley Breweries
PLC
PO Box 26
Park Brewery
Bath Road
Wolverhampton
WV1 4NY

Formed in 1890 by the merger of three
concerns, Banks's has expanded rapidly
to become one of the major regional
brewers. Amongst the several breweries
acquired since 1890, that of Julia Hanson
& Co at Dudley continues to brew,
although the bottled beers come from
the Wolverhampton plant.

Mild Ale
ABV 3.5%   1pt NRB
Old Ale
ABV 9.1%   ⅓pt
Shandy
ABV 1%   ½pt

Bass

Bass Brewers Limited
137 High Street
Burton upon Trent
Staffs
DE14 1JZ

Britain's largest brewing combine, Bass is
well known for having registered the first
trademark — its famous red triangle

motel. Not so well known is the fact that the diamond on the label of Bass No 1 is the second trade mark to be registered. Bass merged with its nearby rivals Worthington in 1927; other major mergers included the tie-up with Mitchells & Butlers, before merging with the Charrington United Breweries group to form the present company.

Sweetheart Stout is the sole reminder of the Younger Brewery at Alloa, not to be confused with William Younger of Edinburgh, which is now part of the Scottish & Newcastle group. Similarly, Fowlers Wee Heavy is the last remnant of the product range of the John Fowler brewery, founded in Prestonpans in 1720 and absorbed into Northern Breweries (itself a Bass constituent) in 1960.

Sweetheart Stout
ABV 2.0% $\frac{1}{2}$pt   1956
Toby Brown Ale
ABV 2.8% $\frac{1}{2}$pt   late 1960s
Jubilee Stout
ABV 3.0% $\frac{1}{2}$pt   1935
Bass Light Ale
ABV 3.1 $\frac{1}{2}$pt,1pt
Toby Ale
ABV 3.1% $\frac{1}{2}$pt   19th century
Toby Light
ABV 3.1% $\frac{1}{2}$pt   late 1960s
Bass Pale Ale
ABV 3.4% $\frac{1}{2}$pt
Bass Blue
ABV 3.7% $\frac{1}{2}$pt   1930s
Carling Black Label
ABV 4.1% $\frac{1}{2}$pt
Tennents Lager
ABV 4.1% $\frac{1}{2}$pt,1pt   1885

Hoopers Ginger Brew
ABV 4.7%   ⅓ litre   1994

Carling Red
ABV 4.8%   1993

Gold Bier
ABV 5.0%   ⅓ litre   1990

Lamot Pils
ABV 5.0%   ½pt

Poker Alice
ABV 5.0%   ⅓ litre   1993

Bass Distinction
ABV 5.1%   ⅓ litre   1993

Black Dove
ABV 5.1%   ⅓ litre   1994

Tennents Dry
ABV 5.5%   ⅓ litre   1994

Carling XD
ABV 5.5%   ⅓ litre

White Shield
ABV 5.6%   ½pt   19th century

Fowlers Wee Heavy
ABV 7.1%   ⅓pt
Tennents Super
ABV 9.0%   ½pt
Bass No 1
ABV 9.0%   ⅓pt   19th century
Barbican
ABV 0%   ⅓ pt
Bass LA
ABV 1.0%   ½ pt

Bateman's

George Bateman & Son Ltd
Salem Bridge Brewery
Wainfleet
Skegness
Lincolnshire
PE24 4JE

One of the UK's best-loved traditional
brewers, Bateman's began brewing in

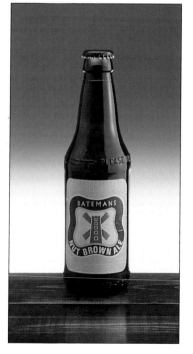

1874. Divisions within the Bateman
family led to the prospect of the company
being sold to the highest bidder in the
mid-1980s and Chairman and Managing
Director George Bateman fought a hard
battle to retain its independence, Victory
Ale being a celebration of the settling of
the differences.

Sainsbury Premium Ale is brewed
exclusively for the supermarket chain.

Nut Brown
ABV 3.0%   ½pt   1935
IPA
ABV 3.8%   ½pt   1935
XXXB Export Ale
ABV 4.8%   ½ litre   1989
Sainsbury Premium Ale
ABV 4.8%   ½ litre   1992
Victory Ale
ABV 6.0%   ½ litre   1989

Batham's

Daniel Batham & Son
Delph Brewery
Brierley Hill
West Midlands
DY5 2TN

Dating from 1877, this small Black Country firm had not produced any bottled beer since the early 1950s, until its Best Bitter made its appearance in bottles seven years ago.

Best Bitter
ABV 4.3%   1pt   1987

Belhaven

The Belhaven Brewery Company
Spott Road
Belhaven
Dunbar
East Lothian
EH42 1RS

Dating from 1719, Belhaven traded under the name of Dudgeon & Co for many years until the 1970s. Its Export is available in off-licences throughout the country.

Belhaven Pale Ale
ABV 2.7%   1pt   1978
Belhaven Scottish Lager
ABV 3.8%   ½pt   1990
Belhaven Export
ABV 3.9%   1pt   1978
Belhaven Premium Lager
ABV 4.1%   1pt   1982
St Andrews Ale
ABV 4.6%   1pt   1993
Belhaven LA Lager
ABV 1.2%   ½pt   1991

Black Sheep
The Black Sheep Brewery PLC
Wellgarth
Masham
Ripon
North Yorkshire
HG4 4EN

Founded by Paul Theakston of the renowned Masham brewing family in 1992 (see Scottish & Newcastle), both bottled beers are essentially the same product. The Traditional Yorkshire Bitter is a Marks & Spencer own label.

Black Sheep Ale
ABV 4.4%   ½ litre   1992
Traditional Yorkshire Bitter
ABV 4.4%   ⅓ litre   1992

Bodicote
Bodicote Brewery
Plough Inn
Bodicote, Banbury
Oxon
OX15 4BZ

A home-brew pub since 1982, Bodicote's No 9 is occasionally hand bottled as a bottle-conditioned beer. The possibility of installing a bottling line for regular bottling is being investigated.

No 9
ABV 4.2%   ½pt   1988

Borve
Borve Brew House
Ruthven
By Huntly
Aberdeenshire
AB54 4SR

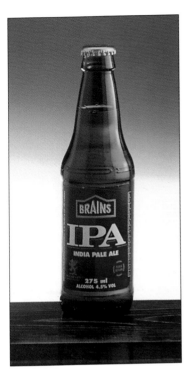

Brain's

S. A. Brain & Co Ltd
The Old Brewery
49 St Mary Street
Cardiff
CF1 1SP

Beer has been brewed at the Old Brewery since at least 1713, but the site was not taken over by S. A. Brain until 1882. Until recent times Brain's produced six bottled products, this has been whittled down to just the one.

IPA
ABV 4.5%   ½pt   early 1950s

Broughton

Broughton Brewery Ltd
Biggar
Lanarkshire
ML12 6HQ

Originally set up on the Isle of Lewis, the Borve Brew House now has a pub alongside. The beers are filtered but not pasteurised and are available bottle-conditioned on request at 14 days notice. Borve Ale is also sold in ½pt bottles at the Minmore House Hotel, Glenlivet as a house beer.

Borve Ale
ABV 4.0%   1pt   1984
Tall Ships IPA
ABV 5.0%   1pt   1991
Union Street 200
ABV 5.0%   1pt   1994
Borve Extra Strong Ale
ABV 10.0%   ½pt   1984

An early example of a new brewery to produce bottled beer, Broughton's Greenmantle Ale appeared in bottle two years after the firm was set up. Its bottled brews are now sold countrywide.

Scottish Oatmeal Stout
ABV 3.8% $\frac{1}{2}$ litre NRB   1992
Greenmantle Ale
ABV 3.9%   1pt & $\frac{1}{2}$ litre NRB   1982
Greenmantle Extra
ABV 4.2 $\frac{1}{2}$ litre NRB   1991
Old Jock
ABV 6.7% $\frac{1}{2}$pt NRB   1984

Burton Bridge
Burton Bridge Brewery
24 Bridge Street
Burton upon Trent
Staffs
DE14 1SY

A bottle-conditioned beer, Burton Bridge's Porter comes in bottles without labels. The details of the beer and brewery are simply applied with a rubber stamp to a patch of yellow paint on the bottle. The brewery began operations in 1982.

Porter
ABV 4.5%   1pt   1983

Butterknowle
Butterknowle Brewery
The Old School House
Lynesack
Bishop Auckland
County Durham
DL13 5QF

Operational since 1990, the Butterknowle Brewery's bottle-conditioned High Force is its first bottled beer. Other bottle-conditioned products may follow.

High Force
ABV 6.2%   due for launch 1995

Cain's
Robert Cain & Company Ltd
The Robert Cain Brewery
Stanhope Street
Liverpool
L8 5XJ

Dating from 1850, the Robert Cain Brewery was acquired by Higsons in 1920, and was closed in 1990 when the latter company was in turn taken over by Boddingtons of Salford. Canned beer was then produced by GB Breweries at the plant, but draught beer and now a bottled version of the canned Formidable Ale, have followed.

Formidable Ale
ABV 5.0% $\frac{1}{3}$ litre   1994

Caledonian

The Caledonian Brewing Company Ltd
Slateford Road
Edinburgh
EH11 1PH

Founded in 1869 as Lorimer & Clark, the brewery continued to trade as such after being acquired by Vaux in 1919. It was purchased from Vaux in a management buyout in 1987, and its Golden Promise

was Britain's first organic beer, winning a Soil Association award in 1993.

70/- Amber Ale			
ABV 3.35%	½ litre	1987	
Golden Pale			
ABV 4.0%	½ litre	1994	
80/- Export Ale			
ABV 4.05%	½ litre	1987	
Tesco Premium Ale			
ABV 4.1%	½ litre		
Deuchars IPA			
ABV 4.6%	½ litre	1994	
Merman Export			
ABV4.8%	½ litre	1994	

Golden Promise
ABV 5.0% $\frac{1}{2}$ litre   1989
Tesco Organic Beer Nature's Choice
ABV 5.0% $\frac{1}{2}$ litre
Edinburgh Strong Ale
ABV 6.4% $\frac{1}{2}$ litre   1988

Carlsberg-Tetley

Carlsberg-Tetley
107 Station Street
Burton upon Trent
Staffs
DE14 1BZ

Created by the merger of Allied Breweries (itself a merger of Ind Coope, Ansells and Tetley Walker) with the Danish brewer Carlsberg, Carlsberg-Tetley brews quite a limited range of bottled beers, considering its 13 different brewery identities still maintained, from Alloa in the north to Friary Meux in Surrey. The Alloa beers are brewed at the Alloa Brewery in Clackmannanshire, the remainder are brewed at Burton upon Trent. The Nicholson's Strong Ale has a back label depicting each pub of the small London chain in which it is sold.

Alloa Sweet Stout
ABV 2.0% $\frac{1}{2}$pt
Brown Peter
ABV 2.8% $\frac{1}{2}$pt
Tetley Brown Ale
ABV 2.8% $\frac{1}{2}$pt
Alloa Original Light
ABV 2.8% $\frac{1}{2}$pt
Ind Coope Light Ale
ABV 3.0% $\frac{1}{2}$pt
Friary Meux Light Ale
ABV 3.0% $\frac{1}{2}$pt
Tetley Special Pale Ale
ABV 3.0% $\frac{1}{2}$pt
Trent Bitter
ABV3.0%   2 litre PET
Tuborg Gold
ABV 5% $\frac{1}{2}$pt

Carlsberg Elephant Beer
ABV 7.2% $\frac{1}{3}$ litre
Maltsman Lager
ABV 4.8% $\frac{1}{3}$ litre
Maltsman Export
ABV 4.8% $\frac{1}{2}$pt
Rhino Lager
ABV $\frac{1}{3}$ litre
Carlsberg Pilsner Lager
ABV 3.4% $\frac{1}{2}$pt
Skol Lager
ABV 3.6% $\frac{1}{2}$pt
Double Diamond
ABV 4.0% $\frac{1}{2}$pt
Alloa Export
ABV 4.2% $\frac{1}{2}$pt
Carlsberg Export
ABV 4.7% $\frac{1}{3}$ litre

BREWED IN SCOTLAND

ALLOA EXPORT

80/-
ALE

Brewed in Alloa, Clackmannanshire
by the Alloa Brewery Company Ltd.

A Quality Product

275ml   alc. 4.2% vol.

Allsopps Export Lager
ABV 4.8% $^1/_3$ litre
Skol Special Strength
ABV 4.8% $^1/_3$ litre
Lowenbrau Special Export
ABV 5.2% $^1/_3$ litre
Nicholson's Strong Ale
ABV 5.2% $^1/_3$ litre
Export Bitter
ABV 5.5% $^1/_2$pt
Export Pale
ABV 5.5% $^1/_2$pt
Lowenbrau Pils
ABV 6.0% $^1/_2$pt
Skol Extra Strength 1080
ABV 8.5%
Carlsberg Special Brew
ABV 9.0% $^1/_2$pt 1959

Swan Light
ABV 0.9% $^1/_2$pt
Dansk LA
ABV 0.9% $^1/_2$pt
St Christopher
ABV 0.5% $^1/_2$pt

Chiltern
Chiltern Brewery
Nash Lee Road
Terrick
Aylesbury
Buckinghamshire
HP17 0TQ

Commencing operations in 1980, the Chiltern Brewery produces beer-related products such as hop-pickled onions and barley wine cake, as well as its draught and bottled beers. Bodgers Barley Wine is bottle-conditioned. Each bottle of Chiltern beer is individually numbered.

Three Hundreds Old Ale
ABV 4.9% 1pt 1989
Bodgers Barley Wine
ABV 8.5% $^1/_2$pt 1990

Commercial Brewery
Commercial Brewing Co Ltd
Worth Brewery
Worth Way
Keighley
West Yorkshire
BD21 5LP

This new brewery began draught beer production as recently as early 1992, and a wide range of bottled products have followed quickly, all of which are bottle-conditioned.

Alesman Traditional Bitter
ABV 3.7% $^1/_2$pt & 1pt 1992
Worth Best Bitter
ABV 4.5% $^1/_2$pt 1993

Worth Porter
ABV 4.6% ½pt & 1pt 1992

Old Toss
ABV 6.5% ½pt 1992

Master James Strong
ABV 8.0% ½pt 1992

Santa's Toss 92
ABV 8.0% ½pt 1992

Santa's Toss 93
ABV 8% ½pt 1993

The basis of today's Courage organisation was the merger in 1955 of the London concerns Barclay Perkins and Courage & Co. The early 1960s saw regional brewers Simonds of Reading and Georges of Bristol join, while in 1970 and 1971 John Smiths and Plymouth Breweries were absorbed into the company. For many years Courage was owned by Imperial Tobacco, before being sold in 1988 to Elders IXL of Australia, which was itself acquired by the Fosters Brewing Group a year later. In 1991 Courage swapped its tied estate with Grand Metropolitan for the latter's brewing organisation, the old Watney Mann Truman group.

Courage
Courage Ltd
Ashby House
1 Bridge Street
Staines
Middlesex
TW18 4TP

Courage Light Ale
ABV 3.2%   ½pt

Websters Green Label Pale Ale
ABV 3.9%   ½pt

John Courage
ABV 4.2%   ½pt

Budweiser
ABV 5.0%   ½pt

Foster's Export
ABV 5.0%   ⅓ litre

Kronenbourg 1664
ABV 5.0%   ⅓ litre

Molson Special Dry
ABV 5.5%   ⅓ litre

Bulldog Strong Ale
ABV 6.3%   ⅓ litre

AKA
ABV 7.5%   ⅓ litre

Imperial Russian Stout
ABV 10.0%   ⅓pt   c1800

John Smith's LA
ABV 0.9%   ½pt

Craven
Craven Wines
Leeds
LS12 6HJ

A packaged beer available through the off-trade.

Challenge Bitter
ABV 3.0%   2 litre PET

Crown Buckley
Crown Buckley
Cowbridge Road
Pontyclun
Mid Glamorgan
CF7 9YG

Created by the merger in 1989 of the Crown Brewery (founded in 1919 as the South Wales & Monmouthshire United Clubs Brewery) and Buckleys (established in 1767), Crown Buckley was at first owned by Guinness but is now fully independent after a management buyout in 1993. None of the Crown bottled beers have survived, but Crown Buckley is notable in being the only brewery still to sell beer in quart flagons.

Buckley's Brown
ABV 3.4%   ½pt, 1pt

Buckley's Bitter
ABV 3.4%   ½pt, 1pt, qrt

Reverend James Original Ale
ABV 4.5%   ½pt   1991

Donnington
Donnington Brewery
Stow on the Wold
Glos
GL54 1EP

Owned by the Arkell family since 1827, the former watermill at Stow on the Wold has been a brewery since 1865. The buildings date back to the 13th century, and the Donnington Brewery is often described as the country's most picturesque.

Brown Ale
ABV 3.5%   ½pt   at least 60 yrs

Light Ale
ABV 3.5%   ½pt   at least 60 yrs

Double Donn
ABV 3.8%   ½pt   at least 60 yrs

Eldridge Pope
Eldridge Pope & Co PLC
Weymouth Avenue
Dorchester
Dorset
DT1 1QT

Dating from 1837, the brewery is famous for its Thomas Hardy's Ale which is Britain's strongest bottle-conditioned beer. The Hardy Country is also bottle-

conditioned. The brewery's light ale was
the last in the UK to have the once-
common 'Crystal' appellation, but
Brewer James' Crystal Ale from Hanseatic
has recently appeared.

Thomas Hardy's Ale
ABV 12.0% $\frac{1}{3}$pt   1968
Crystal LA
ABV 1.0% $\frac{1}{2}$pt   1989

Crystal Light Ale
ABV 3.0% $\frac{1}{2}$pt   1928
Green Top Export Ale
ABV 3.8% $\frac{1}{2}$pt   1965
Hardy Country
ABV 4.2%   1pt   1993
Faust Diat Pils
ABV 4.5% $\frac{1}{2}$pt   1980
Royal Oak
ABV 4.8% $\frac{1}{3}$ litre   1975

Elgoods

Elgood & Sons Ltd
North Brink Brewery
Wisbech
Cambs

The attractive brewery on Wisbech's North Brink was established in 1795 and has traded as Elgoods since 1878.

Pale Ale
ABV 2.6% $\frac{1}{2}$pt   1878
North Brink Porter
ABV 5.0% $\frac{1}{3}$ litre   1993
Highway
ABV 1.0% $\frac{1}{3}$ litre   1985

Enville

Enville Ales
Cox Green
Enville
Stourbridge
West Midlands
DY7 5LG

A year after its first draught brew, Enville has launched its Gothic Ale in green champagne-style bottles, sealed with a cork. The Gothic is bottle-conditioned and is a black beer in the style of old West Midlands Dinner Ales.

Gothic Ale
ABV 5.2% $\frac{1}{3}$ litre, $\frac{3}{4}$ litre 1994

Everards

Everards Brewery Ltd
Castle Acres
Narborough
Leicester
LE9 5BY

Independent brewer which once produced a range of bottled products and which has re-entered the bottled market with one brew so far.

Daredevil
ABV 7.1% $\frac{1}{2}$ litre   1993

Federation

Northern Clubs Federation Brewery Ltd
Lancaster Road
Dunston
Tyne & Wear
NE11 9JR

The brewery moved to its present site in 1980. High Level Brown (named after the famous bridge in Newcastle) has reverted to its original name, after being called Dark Brown and simply Brown Ale for some years. Its label has won the Labologist's Label of the Year award.

Special Ale
ABV 4.0%   1pt
High Level Brown
ABV 4.7%   1pt
LCL Pils
ABV 5.0% $\frac{1}{2}$pt   1980
Export IPA
ABV % $\frac{1}{2}$pt   1968

Fowler (see **Bass**)

Fuller's

Fuller, Smith & Turner PLC
Griffin Brewery
Chiswick Lane
Chiswick
London
W4 2QB

Dating from round 1660, the brewery is one of only two established independent brewers in the London area. (The other is Young's.) The Fuller family has been involved with the firm since 1829, and the Smith and Turner of the company's full title became involved in 1845. Members of the Fuller and Turner families continue to be at the heart of the business.

The Pale Ale was formerly known as Light Ale and before that was called Dinner Ale. London Pride was formerly called Chiswick Pride.

Brown Ale
ABV 3.2%   ½pt   c1930s
Pale Ale
ABV 3.2%   ½pt   c1930s
Chiswick Bitter
ABV 3.2%   2 litre PET
London Pride
ABV 4.7%   ½pt, 1pt, 2 litre PET
ESB Export
ABV 5.9%   ½pt, ⅓ litre, 1pt
                          1986

Golden Pride
ABV 9.2%   ½pt   1967

Gale's

George Gale & Co Ltd
The Hampshire Brewery
Horndean
Hants
PO8 0DA

Dating from 1847, although the current brewery was built in 1869, the firm's bottle-conditioned Prize Old Ale is justly renowned. Hand-bottled, it is unique in being sold in corked bottles of a traditional design. The rest of Gale's bottled portfolio has a less assured future and its Nourishing Stout was discontinued in 1993. The Nut Brown and Light Ale were brewed for Gale's by Gibbs Mew at the time of writing, but their future was under review.

Nut Brown
ABV 2.9%   ½pt   early 20th century

Light Ale
ABV 2.9%   ½pt   early 20th century

HXB
ABV 7.0%   ⅓pt

Prize Old Ale
ABV 9.0%   ½pt   between the wars

Wyvern
ABV 1.0%   ½pt   1980s

Gibbs Mew

Gibbs Mew PLC
Anchor House
Netherhampton Road
Salisbury
Wilts
SP2 8RA

Formed in 1898 by the merger of the companies Bridger Gibbs and Herbert Mew, Gibbs Mew has had a chequered history in the last 30 years, its Bishop's Tipple being available across the country in off-licences. Gibbs Mew has produced bottled beers since 1910 and the Moonraker Brown and Light Ale may well date back to this period. The Light Ale was for many years known as 'GM' and until recently was sold as 'Pale Ale', the change to 'Light' being simply one of marketing, not of recipe. Bishop's Tipple is bottled for Gibbs Mew by the Redruth Brewery and the other two are bottled by Eldridge Pope (qv).

Moonraker Brown Ale
ABV 3.0% $\frac{1}{2}$pt   pre-war
Light Ale
ABV 3.0% $\frac{1}{2}$pt   pre-war
The Bishop's Tipple
ABV 6.5% $\frac{1}{3}$ litre

Greene King
Greene King PLC
Westgate Brewery
Bury St Edmunds
Suffolk
IP33 1QT

Burgeoning regional brewer Greene King has absorbed a number of smaller breweries over the years. Two of these constituents' bottled beers, Pelham Ale (inherited from Rayments) and Crown (from Wells & Winch) survive and despite rationalisation of the range in the 1980s nine brews continue to be bottled. An alternative embossed bottle was introduced for Abbot in 1993.

Burton Ale
ABV 3.0% $\frac{1}{2}$pt   1968

Harvest Sweet Brown
ABV 3.0% $\frac{1}{2}$pt, 1pt

Pale Ale
ABV 3.0% $\frac{1}{2}$pt, 1pt

Pelham Ale
ABV 3.0% $\frac{1}{2}$pt

Crown Ale
ABV 4.0% $\frac{1}{2}$pt   1950

Abbot Ale
ABV 5.0% $\frac{1}{2}$pt, $\frac{1}{3}$ litre   1950s

Strong Suffolk
ABV 6.0% $\frac{1}{2}$pt

St Edmund
ABV 6.3% $\frac{1}{2}$pt   1970

Lowes
ABV 1.0% $\frac{1}{2}$pt   1980s

Grolsch-Ruddles
The Grolsch-Ruddles Brewing Company
Savoy Chambers
8-10 London Street
Andover
Hampshire
SP10 2PA

The former Ruddles brewery of Langham in Rutland has had possibly the most eventful history of any in the last 20 years. Founded in 1858, the company sold its tied estate in 1978, using the money to expand into selling

packaged beer to supermarkets. Sale of the firm to Grand Metropolitan saw the two beers taking a massive presence in pubs in draught form and in shops in bottled and canned form. Both beers are available in packs of four squat ring-pull bottles. Passing to Courage, the firm was sold to Grolsch NV in 1992. The intention is to launch further Ruddles beers, which despite the Hampshire address, are still brewed at Langham.

Best Bitter
ABV 3.7%	½pt NRB	1986

County
ABV 4.9%	½pt NRB	1978

Guernsey Brewery
The Guernsey Brewery Co (1920) Ltd
South Esplanade
St Peter Port
Guernsey
Channel Islands
GY1 1BJ

The larger of Guernsey's two breweries and picturesquely situated on the South Esplanade at St Peter Port, the brewery was originally called the London Brewery and was founded in 1856.

Brown Ale
og 1039	½pt	1940s

Pony Ale
ABV 3.7%	½pt, 1pt, 2 litre PET	1920s

IPA
ABV 4.2%	½pt, 1pt, 2 litre PET	1920s

Milk Stout
og 1042	½pt, 1pt	end of World War 1

Stein Lager
og 1047	½pt	

Guinness
Guinness Brewing
Park Royal Brewery
London
NW10 7RR

Ever increasing trade led to the opening of a Guinness brewery in England in 1936, and technically Guinness Original dates from this time as a British bottled beer. It has of course been available since the founding of the company in 1759.

Guinness Original
ABV 4.3%	½pt, 1pt	1936 (at Park Royal)

Harp Lager
ABV 3.0%	½pt	c1961

Harp Premier
ABV 5.0%	⅓ litre	1986

Satzenbrau Diat Pils
ABV 5.5%	½pt

Kaliber
ABV 1.0%	½pt	1980s

Hall & Woodhouse

Hall & Woodhouse Ltd
The Brewery
Blandford Forum
Dorset
DT11 9LS

Having ceased bottling itself, Hall &
Woodhouse's one bottled beer has been
produced by Eldridge Pope in recent
years. Hall & Woodhouse products are
often known as 'Badger Beers' — the
John Brown label includes a Badger
motif. The company was due to launch a
new bottled beer range in 1994.

John Brown Ale
ABV 3.0%   ¹/₂pt   1980

Hanseatic

Hanseatic Trading Company
North Stables
Casewick Park
Casewick
Stamford
Lincolnshire
PE99 4RX

Its products initially available through the
Oddbins off-licence chain, the Hanseatic
Trading Co now supplies its beers to a
wide segment of the off-trade. The Black
Russian is a reconstruction of a pre-1914
beer and uses brown malt. The Hanseatic
beers are not fined, enabling them to be
consumed by vegans. Hanseatic does not
brew itself — the beers, all of which are
bottle-conditioned, are produced by
McMullen (qv).

BCA
ABV 4.5%   ¹/₂ litre   1993
Brewer James' Crystal Ale
ABV4.4%   ¹/₂ litre   1994
IPA
ABV 4.5%   ¹/₂ litre   1993

Vassilenski's

Чёрное Русское Пиво

~ *Black Russian*

A Bottle-Conditioned Beer

500 ml   alc 4.8% vol

Sainsbury's Bottle Conditioned Ale
ABV 4.5%   1994
Vassilenski's Black Russian
ABV 4.8%   ½ litre   1993

Hardington
Hardington Brewery
Albany Buildings
Dean Lane
Bedminster
Bristol
BS3 1BT

Founded in 1991, Hardington has produced a bottled version of its draught Old Ale. Further bottled products may follow.

Hardington Old Ale
ABV 6.5%   ⅓ litre   1994

Harvey's
Harvey & Son (Lewes) Ltd
The Bridge Wharf Brewery
6 Cliffe High Street
Lewes
East Sussex
BN7 2AH

One of Britain's great traditional brewers, Harvey's dates from around 1790 and produces a splendid range of bottled beers as wide as its comprehensive draught portfolio. Now one of few of the old-established independents to brew its own stout, the company's products have chalked up an impressive list of awards. The Tom Paine is bottle-conditioned.

Sweet Sussex Stout
ABV 2.8%   ½pt   1964
Nut Brown
ABV 3.0%   ½pt, 1pt   1920s
India Pale Ale
ABV 3.2%   ½pt, 1pt   1920s
Blue Label
ABV 3.6%   ½pt   1956
Exhibition Brown Ale
ABV 3.6%   ½pt   1964
Armada Ale
ABV 4.5%   ½pt   1988
Porter
ABV 4.8%   ½pt   1993
Tom Paine
ABV 5.5%   1pt   1991
Elizabethan Ale
ABV 8.1%   ⅓pt   1953
Christmas Ale
ABV 8.1%   ½pt   1972
Bill Brewer
ABV 1.0%   ½pt   1989
John Hop
ABV 1.0%   ½pt   1988

Heritage
Heritage Brewery
Thomas Sykes Inn
Anglesey Road
Burton on Trent
Staffs
DE14 3PF

Initially called Foundation Ale, Thomas Sykes Ale is unique in using the 'reputed

pint' size bottle of 13⅓fl oz.
The bottles are individually
corked on a Victorian
corking machine and the
bottle-conditioned brew can
be kept for 25 years.

Thomas Sykes Ale
ABV 10%   Rept'd pt   1986

Hilden
Hilden Brewery
Hilden House
Lisburn
Co. Antrim
BT27 4TY

The first and only cask ale brewery to be set up in Northern Ireland in recent years, the company marketed its Hilden Ale in bottle-conditioned form for a short period at the end of the 1980s. Plans were afoot in 1994 to re-enter the bottled beer market with filtered beers, but at the time of going to press no further details were available.

Just over a year after commencing brewing draught beer, the Hog's Back Brewery produced its first bottled brew, A over T, standing for 'Aromas over Tongham'.

Olde Swine
ABV 6.0%	$\frac{1}{2}$pt	1994

A over T
ABV 9.0%	$\frac{1}{2}$pt	1993

Hog's Back

Hog's Back Brewery
Manor Farm
The Street
Tongham
Surrey
GU10 1DE

Holden's

Holden's Brewery Ltd
Hopden Brewery
George Street
Woodsetton
Dudley
West Midlands
DY1 4LN

Beginning as a home brew pub in 1877, Holden's now supplies a Black Country tied estate of 21 pubs as well as bottling for a number of other breweries, including the Orkney Brewery (qv). The Hazledown Stout and Hazledown Bitter are an inheritance from the closed Davenports Brewery of Birmingham and are brewed for Mason's of Smethwick.

Hazledown Stout
ABV 3.4%   ½pt   1990
Hazledown Bitter
ABV 3.5%   ½pt, 1pt   1990
Holden's Mild
ABV 3.7%   ½pt, 1pt   1954
Holden's Golden
ABV 3.9%   ½pt, 1pt   1954
Holden's Special Bitter
ABV 5.0%   ⅓ litre   1976
Holden XL
ABV 8.9%   ½pt   1954

Holt's
Joseph Holt PLC
Derby Brewery
Empire Street
Cheetham
Manchester
M3 1JD

A resolutely traditional brewery established in 1849, Holt's is well known for the reasonable prices of its products.

Brown Stout
ABV 3.5%   ½pt   pre-World War 1
Pale Ale
ABV 3.6%   ½pt   pre-World War1
Sixex
ABV 6.0%   ⅓pt   pre-World War 1

Hook Norton
The Hook Norton Brewery Co Ltd
The Brewery
Hook Norton
Banbury
Oxon
OX15 5NY

Brewing began at the current brewery's predecessor in 1850 but expansion led to the construction of the current attractive tower brewery at the turn of the century. Power is still provided by a steam engine installed at this time.

Hook Ale
ABV 2.9%   ½pt
Jackpot
ABV 3.3%   ½pt

Best Bitter
ABV 3.3%   2 litre plastic NRB
Old Hooky
ABV 5.5% $^1/_2$ litre NRB

Hop Back
Hop Back Brewery
27 Estcourt Road
Salisbury
Wilts
SP1 3AS

Dating from 1987, this expanding brewery was planning to make its Entire Stout available in bottle-conditioned form during 1994. The details below are, however, provisional.

Entire Stout
ABV 4.8%   1pt   1994

Jennings
Jennings Bros PLC
Castle Brewery
Cockermouth
Cumbria
CA13 9NE

Another brewery which has returned to the bottled beer market after some years, Jennings was at the time of writing also considering bottling its Snecklifter draught beer.

Cumbrian Ale
ABV 4.2% $^1/_3$ litre   1988

Jolly Roger
Jolly Roger Brewery
Globe House
31-33 Friar Street
Worcester
WR1 2NA

Its Winter Wobbler formerly available in $^1/_2$ pint bottles, this 1982-established brewer is relaunching its bottled activities in unusual bottles specially imported from Belgium. Difficulties with securing the supply of these bottles has pushed back the date for the launch from the beginning of 1994 to later in the year.

King & Barnes
King & Barnes Ltd
The Horsham Brewery
18 Bishopric
Horsham
West Sussex
RH12 1QP

An amalgamation of the two firms of King & Sons and Barnes in 1906, the ancestors of these two firms go back nearly two centuries. The Sussex was previously known as Light Ale, and before that as India Pale Ale.

Sussex
ABV 3.5% $^1/_2$pt   1880
Festive
ABV 5.0% $^1/_2$pt   1951
Festive
(bottle-conditioned)
ABV 5.3% $^1/_2$pt, 1pt NRB 1993
Christmas Ale
ABV 8.0% $^1/_3$ litre   1993

Lees
J. W. Lees & Co (Brewers) Ltd
Greengate Brewery
Middleton Junction
Manchester
M24 2AX

Established in 1828, two years before the expansion in the brewing industry prompted by the Duke of Wellington's Beerhouse Act, Lees has prospered in the intervening years, and the brewery still remains controlled by descendants of the founder. The Vintage Harvest Ale has been brewed once a year since 1986.

Brown Ale
ABV 3.0% $^{1}/_{2}$pt

Light Ale
ABV 3.5% $^{1}/_{2}$pt

**Archer
Sweet Stout**
ABV 4.0% $^{1}/_{2}$pt

Export Ale
ABV 5.0% $^{1}/_{2}$pt

Edelbrau Diat Pils
ABV 6.0% $^{1}/_{2}$pt   c1980

**Moonraker
Strong Ale**
ABV 7.5% $^{1}/_{2}$pt

Vintage Harvest Ale
ABV 11.5% $^{1}/_{2}$pt   1986

Shandy
ABV 0.9% $^{1}/_{2}$pt

Maclays

Thistle Brewery
Alloa
FK10 1ED

Founded in 1830, the brewery was rebuilt as a typical Victorian tower brewery in 1896. In 1991 it was purchased by Evelyn Matthews and development of its traditional brands, including the bottled products, has taken place.

Export
ABV 4.0%   ½ litre
Oat Malt Stout
ABV 4.5%   ½ litre
Scotch Ale
ABV 5.0%   ½ litre

McMullen

McMullen & Sons Ltd
The Hertford Brewery
26 Old Cross
Hertford
SG14 1RD

The history of McMullen can be traced back to 1827. In addition to its own products, the company brews for the Hanseatic Trading Co (qv).

Mac's Brown
ABV 3.0%   ½pt
                pre-1937
No 1 Pale Ale
ABV 3.8%   ½pt
                c1937

McMULLEN STRONG HART
FULLY MATURED STRONG ALE
MATURED FOR UP TO 1 YEAR
alc 7% vol   170 ml
BREWED IN ENGLAND. McMULLEN & SONS LTD. HERTFORD

Sainsbury's Bottle
Conditioned Ale
ABV 4.5%   ½ litre   1994
Castle
Special Pale Ale
ABV 5.0%   ½pt   c1971
Stronghart
ABV 7.0%   ⅓pt   1989
Crafter LA Bitter
ABV 1.0%   ½pt   1989

Mansfield

Mansfield Brewery PLC
Littleworth
Mansfield
Notts
NG18 1AB

Major regional brewing concern dating from 1855. As well as its estate of public houses and the free on-trade, Mansfield is a major supplier of beer to supermarkets in PET bottles, both under its own brandings (listed below) and under supermarkets' own labels, the origins of which are considered confidential. The company is reckoned to supply about 40% of the supermarkets' own label beers.

Drayman's
Dark Mild
ABV 3.0%   2 litre PET   1986
Drayman's
Best Bitter
ABV 3.0%   2 & 3 litre PET 1986
Jorvic Lager
ABV 3.0%   2 & 3 litre PET 1986
Mansfield
Dark Mild
ABV 3.5%   2 litre PET   1988
Mansfield Bitter
ABV 3.9%   2 litre PET   1988

Marksman Lager

ABV 4.1%	2 litre PET	1987

Goldmark
Super Strength
Lager

ABV 8.5%	$\frac{1}{2}$ litre NRB	1993

Marston's

Marston, Thompson & Evershed Ltd
PO Box 26
Shobnall Road
Burton upon Trent
DE14 2BW

Dating from 1834 when J. Marston & Son was established at Burton upon Trent, the firm amalgamated with John Thompson & Son and moved to its present site in 1898. Amalgamation with Sydney Evershed in 1905 has been followed by fits of expansion which have produced the biggest of the regional brewers. Beer is fermented in the now-unique Union sets of wooden casks, which is the most effective way of sustaining the rather difficult yeast strain essential to the palate of the company's beers.

Low C is a low-calorie beer for those concerned about their weight.

Light Ale

ABV 2.8%	$\frac{1}{2}$pt	many years

Tesco Mild

ABV 3.8%	$\frac{1}{2}$ litre

Marston's
Union Mild

ABV 4.0%	$\frac{1}{2}$ litre	1993

Marston's Stout

ABV 4.0%	$\frac{1}{2}$ litre	1993

Tesco Traditional
Premium Ale

ABV 4.1%	1pt

Low C

ABV 4.2%	$\frac{1}{2}$pt	1970

Albion Porter

ABV 4.4%	$\frac{1}{2}$ litre	1993

Pedigree Imperial Pint

ABV 4.5%	1pt	1993

Marston's India
Export Ale

ABV 5.5%	$\frac{1}{2}$ litre	1993

Owd Roger

ABV 7.6%	$\frac{1}{3}$pt

Mason's

T. Mason & Sons Ltd
Grantham Road
Smethwick
Warley
West Midlands
B66 4NW

The Hazledown Stout and Hazledown Bitter formerly produced by Davenports of Birmingham are now brewed and bottled for Mason's by Holdens (qv).

Morland

Morland & Co PLC
PO Box 5
The Brewery
Ock Street
Abingdon
Oxon
OX14 5DD

Morland dates from 1711. Its most famous brew, which began as a bottled beer, but which is now also popular as draught beer, celebrates Abingdon's 20th century history. Called Old Speckled Hen, it commemorates the fabric bodywork of one of the first MG cars.

Light Ale

ABV 3.5%	$\frac{1}{2}$pt	'many years'

Old Speckled Hen

ABV 5.2%	$\frac{1}{2}$pt, $\frac{1}{2}$ litre NRB	1979

Morrells

Morrells Brewery Ltd
The Lion Brewery
St Thomas' Street
Oxford
OX1 1LA

Morrells began in 1782, but brewing on the site of the Lion Brewery dates back much further, indeed to the 15th century. Still run by the Morrell family, the company remains staunchly independent.

Light Ale
ABV 3.2%   ½pt   late 19th
                                century
Castle Ale
ABV 4.3%   ½pt   1948
Brewery Gate
Bitter
ABV 4.3%   ½ litre NRB   1993
College Ale
ABV 7.4%   ⅓pt   19th
                                century

Nethergate

Nethergate Brewery Co Ltd
11-13 High Street
Clare
Suffolk
CO10 8NY

Founded in 1986 in a former motor vehicle repair workshop in the attractive town of Clare, Nethergate's two bottled beers have a strong presence in supermarkets and off-licences.

Bitter
ABV 4.1%   ½ litre   1992
Old Growler
Special Porter
ABV 5.5%   ½ litre   1992
Sainsbury's
Blackfriars Porter
ABV 5.5%   ½ litre

Nicholson's (see Carlsberg-Tetley)

North Yorkshire

The North Yorkshire Brewing Company
80-84 North Ormesby Road
Middlesbrough
Cleveland
TS4 2AG

This expanding brewery began operations in 1990. Half a dozen draught beers are produced, one of which is available in bottle.

Flying Herbert
ABV 4.5-5.0%   ⅓ litre NRB   1992

Old Luxters

Old Luxters Vinyard, Winery &
Brewhouse
Hambeldon
Henley on Thames
Oxfordshire
RG9 6JW

The Old Luxters organisation embraces a vinyard (planted in 1982) and an art gallery. Barn Ale made its appearance as a bottled beer at the beginning of 1994 and in addition to being available in local pubs was soon exported to France and Sweden. A bottle-conditioned beer, Barn Ale is brewed using pale, crystal and chocolate malts.

Barn Ale
ABV 5.4%   ½ litre   1994

Orkney

The Orkney Brewery
Quoyloo
Sandwick
Orkney
KW16 3LT

Britain's most northerly brewery, its beers are bottled by Holden's (qv).

Randall's

R. W. Randall Ltd
Vauxlaurens Brewery
PO Box 154
Guernsey
GY1 3JG

Although the brewery itself is believed
to date from the 17th century, it was
not bought by the Randall family until
1868. There are 19 tied houses on
Guernsey, but the Stout can be difficult
to find, especially in its ½pint bottle.
The process of brewing low-alcohol
bitter, now adopted by many other
breweries, was pioneered by Randall's
for the launch of its LA.

Original VB

1033og	½pt, 1pt &	
	½ litre NRB	1945

Raven Ale

ABV 3.8%	1pt	1990

Dark Island

ABV 4.6%	1pt	1991

Dragonhead Stout

ABV 4.0%	1pt	1991

Skullsplitter

ABV 8.5%	½pt	1989

Palmer's

J. C. & R. H. Palmer Ltd
Old Brewery
Bridport
Dorset
DT6 4JA

Celebrating its 200th anniversary in 1994,
Palmers is a genuinely traditional family
firm. It is also the only brewery in the UK
to boast a thatched bottling hall!

Light Pale Ale

ABV 3.2%	½pt	1890s

Nut Brown Ale

ABV 3.2%	½pt	1890s

Classic Pale Ale

ABV 4.6%	½pt	1987

Tally Ho!

ABV 4.7%	½pt	1930s

IPA		
1046og	1pt, ½pt and ½ litre NRB	1952
Stout		
1050og	½pt, ½ litre NRB	1945
LA		
ABV 1.0%	½pt	1988

Ridley's

T. D. Ridley & Sons Ltd
Hartford End Brewery
Chelmsford
Essex
CM3 1JZ

Founded in 1842, Ridley's remains staunchly independent. Unlike so many other brewers, it saw an increase in sales of its bottled beers during the 1980s. Bishop's Ale barley wine commemorates Bishop Nicholas Ridley, an ancestor of the brewing family, who was burnt at the stake as Bishop of London in 1555.

Essex Light Ale		
ABV 3.1%	½pt	early 1900s
Essex Brown Ale		
ABV 3.1%	½pt	early 1900s

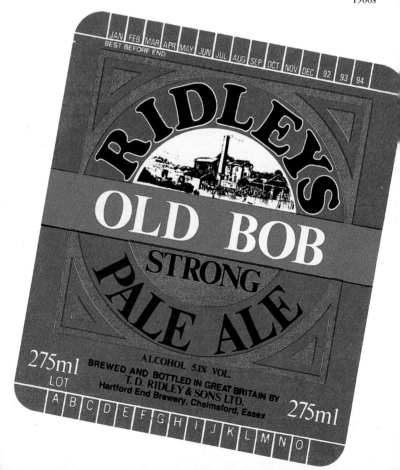

Old Bob
Strong Pale Ale
ABV 5.1%   ¹/₂pt   late 1940s·
Bishop's Ale
ABV 8.0%   ¹/₂pt

Ringwood
Ringwood Brewery
Christchurch Road
Ringwood
Hampshire
BH24 3AP

A pioneer of the new wave of traditional draught beer breweries, being founded in 1978, Ringwood's Old Thumper has won a number of awards in its draught form.

Old Thumper
ABV 5.8%   ½pt NRB   1983
Ringwood Bitter
ABV 3.8%   2 litre PET   1989

Rising Sun

The Rising Sun Inn
Knowle Bank Road
Shraley Brook
Audley
Stoke-on-Trent
Staffordshire
ST7 8DS

The Rising Sun Inn began brewing in 1989 and bottling commenced soon afterwards. Both beers are bottle-conditioned.

Total Eclipse
ABV 6.8%   ½pt   1990
Solar Flare
ABV 11.0%   ½pt   1990

Robinson's
Frederic Robinson Ltd
Unicorn Brewery
Stockport
Cheshire
SK1 1JJ

Founded in 1838, the company began to brew beer at the Unicorn Inn at Stockport in 1865. Steady growth and acquisitions have culminated in a major

regional brewer which is still family-controlled. The Old Tom dates from the commencement of bottling by the company.

Brown Ale
ABV 3.0%   ½pt   1955
Pale Ale
ABV 4.0%   ½pt   1963
Old Tom
ABV 8.5%   ½pt   1908
Wheelwright
ABV 1%   ½pt   1989

Rooster's
Rooster's Brewery
Unit 20
Claro Business Park
Claro Road
Harrogate
North Yorkshire
HG1 4BA

Both the Rooster's Brewery bottled beers are bottle-conditioned. The company began operations in 1992.

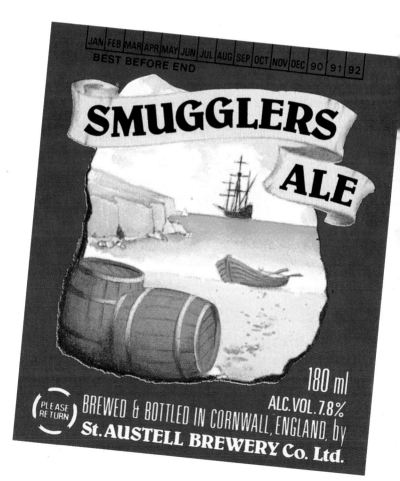

Rooster's
ABV 4.7%   ⅓ litre   1993
Nector
ABV 6.0%   ⅓ litre   1994

Ross Brewing Co
The Bristol Brewhouse
117-119 Stokes Croft
Bristol
BS1 3RW

Initially brewing only bottle-conditioned beers, this firm was set up in 1989. Now concentrating more on draught beer for the pub it has moved to, the remaining bottled beer is produced under contract by Eldridge Pope. A wholly organic beer, Saxon Strong Ale contains organic malt, honey and apple juice.

Saxon Strong Ale
ABV 5.0%   ⅓ litre   1990

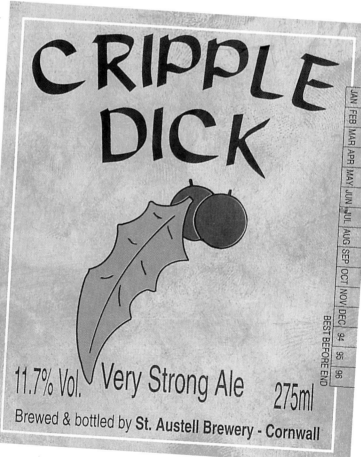

CRIPPLE DICK

11.7% Vol. Very Strong Ale 275ml

Brewed & bottled by St. Austell Brewery - Cornwall

JAN FEB MAR APR MAY JUN JUL AUG SEP OCT NOV DEC   BEST BEFORE END   94 95 96

180 ml   Alc. 11.7% vol.

SPECIAL BARLEY WINE

PRINCE'S

ALE

ST. AUSTELL BREWERY

BREWED IN CORNWALL, ENGLAND

Ruddles — see **Grolsch-Ruddles**

St Austell
St Austell Brewery Company Ltd
63 Trevarthian Road
St Austell
Cornwall
PL25 4BY

Dating back to 1851, the firm has always been run by members of the Hicks family. The Prince's Ale Special Barley Wine is also sold as Cripple Dick in half-pint bottles. During the summer of 1994, the brewery was due to cease undertaking its own bottling, after which its beers will be packaged by Redruth Brewery in half-pint NRBs.

Hicks Strong Ale
ABV 5.0% $\frac{1}{3}$ litre   1991

Smugglers Ale
ABV 7.8% $\frac{1}{3}$pt   1948

Prince's Ale Special Barley Wine
ABV 11.7% $\frac{1}{3}$pt   1969

Cripple Dick
ABV 11.7% $\frac{1}{2}$pt

Scottish & Newcastle

Scottish & Newcastle Beer Production Ltd
PO Box 1RA
Newcastle NE99 1RA

Two major regional groups — Scottish Brewers and Newcastle Breweries — merged in 1960 to create the Scottish & Newcastle combine. Scottish Brewers had been formed in the 1930s by the merger of the William McEwan and William Younger breweries in Edinburgh. (The latter should not be confused with the brewery of George Younger of Alloa which after takeover by Northern Breweries in 1960 has been assimilated into the Bass group, whose Sweetheart Stout still bears its name.) On Tyneside, Newcastle Breweries resulted from the merger of five local firms. The 1980s saw the acquisition of the Blackburn firm of Matthew Brown (which had only recently purchased the Theakston brewery at Masham) and the Home Brewery at Daybrook near Nottingham.

In 1994 there are five Scottish & Newcastle breweries in operation, three of which (the Fountain Brewery at Edinburgh, the Home Brewery and the Tyne Brewery) produce bottled beer.

A diverse range of bottled beers is still brewed by this massive organisation, although its Sweet Stout has been a recent casualty. Although more a strong dark ale than a true brown ale, this company's Newcastle Brown Ale is the country's best-selling bottled beer with 10 million pint bottles being sold every year. The recent relaunch of the McEwans bottled range and the introduction of the potent Jamaican Brew illustrate Scottish & Newcastle's participation in the bottled beer revival.

Youngers Pale Ale
ABV 3.1% $\frac{1}{2}$pt   1920s

Youngers Brown Ale
ABV 3.2% $\frac{1}{2}$pt   1920s

Home Luncheon Ale
ABV 3.2%   1pt

McEwans Pale Ale
ABV 3.2%   1pt   1920s

Newcastle Amber Ale
ABV 3.3%   1pt   1920s

Home Brewed
ABV 3.6% $\frac{1}{2}$pt

Home Stout
ABV 3.6% $\frac{1}{2}$pt

Theakston Best Bitter
ABV 3.8%   1pt   1970s

Robin Hood IPA
ABV 4.2% $\frac{1}{2}$pt

McEwans Export
ABV 4.5% $\frac{1}{2}$pt   19th century

McEwans 80/-
ABV 4.5%   1pt   1993

Youngers No3
ABV 4.5%   1pt   1993

Newcastle Brown Ale
ABV 4.7% $\frac{1}{3}$ litre, 1pt   1927

Coors Extra Lager
ABV 5.0% $\frac{1}{3}$ litre

McEwans 90/-
ABV 5.5%   1pt   1993

Theakston Old Peculier
ABV 5.55% $\frac{1}{2}$pt   1970s

Jamaican Very Strong Ale
ABV 8.0% $\frac{1}{2}$pt

Shepherd Neame

Shepherd Neame Ltd
17 Court Street
Faversham
Kent
ME13 7AX

Brewing has been undertaken on the site occupied by Shepherd Neame continuously since 1698, and the company has recently made the ½ litre non-returnable bottles of Bishop's Finger widely available through supermarkets and off-licences. The Kingfisher lager is brewed under licence from United Breweries of Bangalore, India.

Light Ale
ABV 3.2%   ½pt   mid-19th century

Masterbrew
ABV 4.0%   ½ litre   early19th century

Spitfire
ABV 4.7%   ½ litre   1990

Kingfisher Lager
ABV 5.2%   ½ litre   1984

Original Porter
ABV 5.2%   ½ litre   1991

Bishop's Finger
ABV 5.4%   ½pt and ½ litre   1958

Birell
ABV 1.2%   ½pt   1986

Pilgrims
ABV 1.2%   ½pt   1988

Samuel Smith

Samuel Smith Old Brewery (Tadcaster)
Tadcaster
North Yorks
LS24 9SB

Not to be confused with the neighbouring John Smith's brewery, which is part of Courage and was formed after a split in the Smith family, the older of Tadcaster's two breweries has brewed since 1758. An impressive range of bottled products complements the company's famous draught beers. What other brewery has room in its portfolio for three bottled stouts?

Taddy Brown Ale
ABV 3.0%   1pt

Light Ale
ABV 3.3%   ½pt

Pale Ale
ABV 4.1%   1pt

Extra Stout
ABV 4.1%   ½pt

Pure Brewed Lager
ABV 4.5%   ⅓ litre, 1pt

Nut Brown Ale
ABV 5.0%   1pt

Oatmeal Stout
ABV 5.0%   1pt

Old Brewery Strong Pale Ale
ABV 5.0%   1pt

Taddy Porter
ABV 5.0%   1pt

Ayingerbrau 'D' Pils
ABV 5.5%   ½pt

Winter Welcome
ABV 6.0%   1pt

Imperial Stout
ABV 7.0%   ⅓ litre

Ayingerbrau Very Strong Lager
ABV 9.3%   ½pt

Strong Golden Barley Wine
ABV 10.2%   ⅓pt

Shandy
ABV 1.2%   ½pt

Ayingerbrau Low Alcohol Lager
ABV 1%   ½pt

Snowdonia

Snowdonia Brewery
c/o The Bryn Arms
Gellilydan
Gwynedd
LL41 4EH

A home-brew pub in the heart of Snowdonia, the Bryn Arms has recently begun to produce its first bottled beer. Both beers are bottle-conditioned.

Cwrw Trog
ABV 7.0%   ½pt, 1pt   1994
Celt
ABV 8.0%   ½pt   1994

Star & Tipsy Toad
Star & Tipsy Toad Brewery
St Peter's Village
St Peter
Jersey
JE3 7AA

The second Tipsy Toad brewpub, which opened in the middle of St Helier in May 1994, incorporates a small bottling plant.

Tipsy Toad Ale
ABV 4.0%   1pt   1994

Tally Ho
Tally Ho Country Inn & Brewery
14 Market Street
Hatherleigh
Devon
EX20 3JN

A home-brew pub since 1990, the Tally Ho Inn has produced some one-off special brews as well as its regular bottled beers. All its bottled products are bottle-conditioned.

Tarka's Tipple
ABV 5.7%   ⅔pt   1993
Thurgia
ABV 5.7%   ⅔pt   1991
also brews under contract:
Lion Roar
ABV 5.2%   ⅔pt   1993
(available only from Red Lion Deli, Okehampton)

Creber Ale
ABV 6.0%   ⅔pt   1992
(available only from N. H. Creber, Tavistock)

Tennents (see **Bass**)

Timothy Taylor
Timothy Taylor & Co Ltd
Knowle Spring Brewery
Keighley
West Yorks
BD21 1AW

Thoroughly traditional Yorkshire brewery founded in 1858. In its draught form, Landlord is one of the best-known and respected beers in the free trade. Taylor's range has diminished in recent years, its Northerner No 1 Dark Ale, succumbing not long after public endorsement by Edwina Currie MP at a Beer Festival, but two bottled products remain.

Special Pale Ale
ABV 3.3%   ½pt, 1pt   1928
Landlord
ABV 4.1%   ½pt, 1pt   1953

Thwaites
Daniel Thwaites PLC
PO Box 50
Star Brewery
Blackburn
Lancs
BB1 5BU

Dating from 1807 when Daniel Thwaites bought the (already established) brewery, the company has expanded so that it is now a major northwest brewer. Its brewery was completely rebuilt in 1966.

Danny Brown
ABV 3.2%   ½pt

East Lancashire Pale Ale
ABV 3.4% $\frac{1}{2}$pt
Big Ben
ABV 5.0% $\frac{1}{2}$pt
Old Dan
ABV 7.0% $\frac{1}{3}$pt

Titanic

Titanic Brewery
Unit G
Harvey Works
Lingard Street
Burslem
Stoke on Trent
Staffordshire
ST6 1ED

Founded in 1985 and reborn after a period of inactivity, both of the brewery's bottled products are bottle-conditioned.

Victorian Stout
ABV 5.0% $\frac{1}{2}$pt   1993
Christmas Ale
ABV 7.8% $\frac{1}{2}$pt   1992

Tolly Cobbold

Tollemache & Cobbold Brewery Ltd
Cliff Road
Ipswich
Suffolk
IP3 0AZ

Brewing since 1723, with a break in the 1980s when the brewery was closed under the ownership of the Brent Walker group — a time when Tolly beers were brewed at Hartlepool — a management buyout has sparked a renaissance. All the bottled beers now produced were brewed by the old company, Cantab being acquired when the Tollemache brewery took over Cambridge's Star Brewery in 1934. A 'Year Beer' is introduced each year; if it is successful, it

is then maintained as a permanent part of the range. This has been the case with Cobnut, Cantab and Beano stout.

Tolly Light Ale
ABV 3.0% $\frac{1}{2}$pt   1991
Tolly Brown Ale
ABV 3.0% $\frac{1}{2}$pt   1991
Cobnut
ABV 3.2% $\frac{1}{2}$pt   1991
Beano Stout
ABV 4.1% $\frac{1}{2}$pt   1993
Tolly Strong Ale
ABV 4.6% $\frac{1}{3}$ litre   1993
Cantab
ABV 4.6% $\frac{1}{3}$ litre   1992

Traquair House

Traquair House
Innerleithen
Peeblesshire
EH44 6PW

The late Peter Maxwell Stuart, Laird of Scotland's oldest inhabited house, began to brew the bottled ale that bears the house's name on discovering an 18th century brewhouse there in the 1960s. Using the original utensils, and with assistance from Dudgeon (Belhaven), the bottles were originally individually numbered and are sold in a limited number of outlets worldwide.

Traquair House Ale
ABV 7.2% $\frac{1}{3}$ litre   1965

Ushers

Ushers of Trowbridge PLC
Directors House
68 Fore Street
Trowbridge
Wilts
BA14 8JF

Founded in 1824, Ushers was for long a

part of Watneys and latterly Courage before a management buyout in 1992. The famous Mann's Brown, originally brewed in Northampton and formerly also available as a keg beer, was relaunched in 1993 and is brewed to the original recipe.

Mann's Original Brown Ale
ABV 2.8% $\frac{1}{2}$pt, 1pt &
                $\frac{1}{2}$ litre NRB 1902
Light Ale
ABV 3.2% $\frac{1}{2}$pt   1993
Triple Crown
ABV 3.2%   2 litre PET &
                4pt PET   1992
Best
ABV 3.8%   2 litre PET 1992
Founders Ale
ABV 4.5%   2 litre PET &
                4pt PET   1992
1824 Particular
ABV 6.0% $\frac{1}{3}$ litre,
                $\frac{1}{2}$ litre NRB 1993
Dark Horse Porter
ABV 5.0% $\frac{1}{3}$ litre   1993

Vaux
Vaux Breweries Ltd
The Brewery
Sunderland
SR1 3AN

Founded in 1806, Vaux for a time until 1986 operated four breweries, but the closure of the Darley plant at Thorne and the sale of Lorimer & Clark to the Caledonian Brewery (qv) has left just the former Wards brewery in Sheffield and the original Vaux base at Sunderland. Bottled beers are produced only at the latter.

Double Maxim
ABV 4.2%   1pt   1938
Scorpion Dry Lager
ABV 5.0% $\frac{1}{3}$ litre NRB 1991
Maxim Light
ABV 0.9% $\frac{1}{2}$pt   1988

Wadworth's
Wadworth & Co
Northgate Brewery
Devizes
Wiltshire
SN10 1JW

Taking its trademark from the Northgate at Devizes, Wadworth's eponymous brewery is an architectural landmark in its own right. The origins of the firm date back to 1768, but the dates when its three bottled beers were first produced are less clear. They have certainly been produced, says the brewery, 'for at least 20 years'.

Brown Ale
ABV 3.0% $\frac{1}{2}$pt
Light Ale
ABV 3.0% $\frac{1}{2}$pt
Old Timer
ABV 5.5% $\frac{1}{2}$pt & 2 litre PET

Charles Wells
Charles Wells Ltd
The Eagle Brewery
Havelock Street
Bedford
MK40 4LU

Seafaring captain Charles Wells entered the brewing scene in 1876 when he purchased the Horne Lane brewery in Bedford to satisfy his prospective father-in-law, who disapproved of his daughter marrying a sailor. In 1976, a new brewery was built, although water from the Horne Lane site is still used in the brewing process. Red Stripe, Kirin and Chicago Old Gold are brewed under licence from overseas brewers Desnoes & Geddes, Kirin Brewery and My Kinda Town respectively. A pasteurised version of Wells draught Eagle bitter is available in PET bottle.

Charles Wells also sells PET-bottle brews under the name of the Abington Brewery.

Light Ale
ABV 3.0%   ½pt

Kellerbrau
ABV 3.4%   2 litre PET

Eagle Bitter
ABV 3.6%   2 litre PET

Red Stripe Lager
ABV 4.7%   ⅓ litre   1977

Chicago Old Gold
ABV 4.8%   ⅓ litre   1990

Crest Export
ABV 4.8%   ¼ litre   1994

Kirin
ABV 4.8%   ⅓ litre   1992

Bombardier Export
ABV 5.5%   ⅓ litre   1992

as Abington Brewery:
Abington Bitter
ABV 3.0%   3 litre PET

Crest Lager
ABV 3.0%   2 litre PET

West Coast

West Coast Brewing Company Ltd
Kings Arms Hotel
4A Helmshore Walk
Chorlton-on-Medlock
Manchester
M13 9TH

Impressively prolific brewery founded in 1989, which alongside 10 draught beers

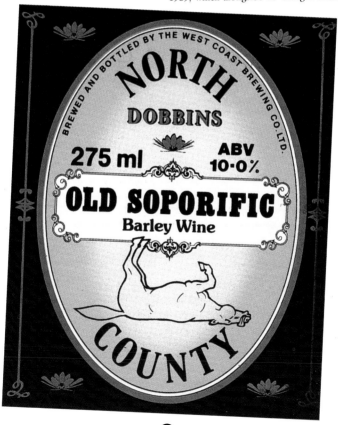

BREWED AND BOTTLED BY THE WEST COAST BREWING CO. LTD.

NORTH
DOBBINS
275 ml   ABV 10·0%
OLD SOPORIFIC
Barley Wine
COUNTY

WARNING: Excessive intake of alcohol is not recommended because you may lose your self control, family, job, health or become an alcoholic

for its two tied houses and the free trade, manages to produce no less than 13 bottled products, which are finding a growing market in the free trade.

Mild

	ABV		
	3.2%	2 litre	1990

	ABV		
Best Bitter	3.7%	1pt	1994
Guiltless Stout	3.8%	1pt	1994
Lager Beer	4.0%	2 litre	1990
Yellow Mountain Beer	4.5%	1/3 litre	1991
Naturally Conditioned Ginger Beer	5.0%	1pt	1992
Yakima Grande Porter	5.5%	1/2 litre	1991
Diat Pils	5.5%	1/2pt	1990
Mittlefrau Pils	5.6%	1/2pt	1990
Yakima Grande Pale Ale	6.0%	1/2 litre	1991
Extra Special Bitter	6.5%	1/2pt	1990
Special Export Lager	8.8%	1/2pt	1990
Old Soporific Barley Wine	10.0%	1/2pt	1992

Whitbread

The Whitbread Beer Company
Porter Tun House
Capability Green
Luton
Beds
LU1 3LS

Massive brewing combine which still produces the bottled beers of a number of its otherwise extinct constituents. Its Mackeson Stout (originally brewed by the firm of Mackeson of Hythe, Kent) and Gold Label barley wine (originally brewed by Tennants of Sheffield) have almost eclipsed the sweet stouts and barley wines of independent brewers across the country.

Forest Brown
ABV 2.7% $\frac{1}{2}$pt, 1pt
Mackeson Stout
ABV 3.0% $\frac{1}{2}$pt, 1pt
Bentleys Bitter
ABV 3.0%   3 litre PET
Light Ale
ABV 3.1% $\frac{1}{2}$pt, 1pt
Double Top
ABV 3.1% $\frac{1}{2}$pt, 1pt
Pale Ale
ABV 3.4% $\frac{1}{2}$pt, 1pt, 2 litre PET
Heineken Lager
ABV 3.4% $\frac{1}{2}$pt
Heldenbrau Lager
ABV 3.5% $\frac{1}{2}$pt
Boddingtons Bitter
ABV 3.8%   2 litre PET
Brewmaster
ABV 3.8% $\frac{1}{2}$pt
Newquay Steam Bitter
ABV 4.0% $\frac{2}{3}$pt
Heineken Export
ABV 5.0% $\frac{1}{3}$ litre
Stella Artois
ABV 5.2% $\frac{1}{3}$ litre
Newquay Steam Lager
ABV 5.3% $\frac{2}{3}$ pt
English Ale
ABV 5.4% $\frac{1}{2}$pt
Stella Dry
ABV 5.5% $\frac{1}{2}$pt
Kaltenberg Diat Pils
ABV 6.0% $\frac{1}{2}$pt
Gold Label
ABV 10.9% $\frac{1}{3}$ pt   1930s
White Label
ABV 1.0% $\frac{1}{2}$pt

Woodforde's
Woodforde's Norfolk Ales
Broadland Brewery
Woodbastwick
Norwich
NR13 6SW

Begun in 1980, Woodforde's moved to its current site in 1989. Norfolk Nips is brewed to a recipe of the old Steward & Patterson Brewery which was closed after absorption into the Watney empire.

Norfolk Nips
ABV 8.5% $\frac{1}{2}$pt   1992

Young's
Young & Co's Brewery PLC
The Ram Brewery
Wandsworth
London
SW18 4JD

Dating from 1675, the Ram Brewery has been associated with the Young family since 1831.
    Oatmeal Stout is now available as a draught beer.

Brown Ale
ABV 3.1% $\frac{1}{2}$pt
Light Ale
ABV 3.2% $\frac{1}{2}$pt
Ram Rod
ABV 4.8% $\frac{1}{2}$pt
Strong Export Bitter
ABV 6.4% $\frac{1}{2}$pt
Old Nick
ABV 6.9% $\frac{1}{2}$pt
Extra Light
ABV 1.0% $\frac{1}{2}$pt
For export:
Oatmeal Stout
ABV 5.0%   12oz   1991

Younger, Alloa (see **Bass**)

Younger, Edinburgh
(see **Scottish & Newcastle**)

Index

Brown Stout	Holt's	57
Buckley's Bitter	Crown Buckley	42
Buckley's Brown	Crown Buckley	42
Budweiser	Courage	42
Bulldog Strong Ale	Courage	42
Burton Ale	Greene King	47
Cantab	Tolly Cobbold	82
Carling Black Label	Bass	29
Carling Red	Bass	30
Carling XD	Bass	30
Carlsberg Export	Carlsberg-Tetley	38
Carlsberg Pilsner Lager	Carlsberg-Tetley	38
Castle Ale	Morrells	66
Castle Special Pale Ale	McMullen	63
Celt	Snowdonia	81
Challenge Bitter	Craven	42
Champion Pale Ale	Adnams	26
Chicago Old Gold	Charles Wells	87
Chiswick Bitter	Fuller's	45
Christmas Ale	Harvey's	51
Christmas Ale	King & Barnes	59
Christmas Ale	Titanic	82
Classic Pale Ale	Palmer's	67
Cobnut	Tolly Cobbold	82
College Ale	Morrells	66
Coors Extra Lager	Scottish & Newcastle	77
County	Grolsch-Ruddles	49
Crafter LA Bitter	McMullen	63
Creber Ale	Tally Ho	81
Crest Export	Charles Wells	87
Crest Lager	Abington/ Charles Wells	87
Cripple Dick	St Austell	77
Crown Ale	Greene King	47
Crystal LA	Eldridge Pope	43
Crystal Light Ale	Eldridge Pope	43
Cumbrian Ale	Jennings	59
Cunning Stunts	Ballards	28
Cwrw Trog	Snowdonia	81
Danny Brown	Thwaites	81
Dansk LA	Carlsberg-Tetley	40
Daredevil Dark	Everards	44
Horse Porter	Ushers	84
Dark Island	Orkney	67
Dark Mild	Mansfield	63
Diat Pils	West Coast	88
Deuchars IPA	Caledonian	37
Distinction	Bass	30
Double Diamond	Carlsberg-Tetley	38
Double Donn	Donnington	42
Double Maxim	Vaux	84
Double Top	Whitbread	89
Dragonhead Stout	Orkney	67
Drayman's Best Bitter	Mansfield	63
Drayman's Dark Mild	Mansfield	63
Eagle Bitter	Charles Wells	87
East Lancashire Pale Ale	Thwaites	82
Edelbrau Diat Pils	Lees	60
Edinburgh Strong Ale	Caledonian	38
Elephant Beer	Carlsberg-Tetley	38
Elizabethan Ale	Harvey's	51
English Ale	Whitbread	89
Entire Stout	Hook Norton	59
ESB	Fuller's	45
Essex Brown Ale	Ridley's	68
Essex Light Ale	Ridley's	68
Exhibition Brown Ale	Harvey's	51

Export	Belhaven	33
Export	Maclays	61
Export Ale	Lees	60
Export Bitter	Carlsberg-Tetley	40
Export IPA	Federation	44
Extra Light	Youngs	89
Export Pale	Carlsberg-Tetley	40
Extra Special Bitter	West Coast	88
Extra Stout	Samuel Smith	79
Extra Strong Ale	Borve	35
Faust Diat Pils	Eldridge Pope	43
Festive	King & Barnes	59
Flying Herbert	North Yorkshire	66
Forest Brown	Whitbread	89
Formidable Ale	Cain's	36
Foster's Export	Courage	42
Founders Ale	Ushers	84
Fowlers Wee Heavy	Bass	31
Friary Meux Light Ale	Carlsberg-Tetley	38
Gold Bier	Bass	30
Gold Label	Whitbread	89
Golden	Holden's	57
Golden Pale	Caledonian	37
Golden Pride	Fuller's	45
Golden Promise	Caledonian	38
Goldmark Super Strength Lager	Mansfield	64
Gothic Ale	Enville	44
Greenmantle Ale	Broughton	92
Greenmantle Extra	Broughton	92
Green Top Export Ale	Eldridge Pope	43
Guiltless Stout	West Coast	88
Hardy Country	Eldridge Pope	43
Harp Lager	Guinness	49
Harp Premier	Guinness	49
Harvest Sweet Brown	Greene King	47
Hazledown Bitter	Holden's	57
Hazledown Stout	Holden's	57
Heineken	Whitbread	89
Heineken Export	Whitbread	89
Heldenbrau	Whitbread	89
Hick's Strong Ale	St Austell	77
High Force	Butterknowle	36
High Level Brown Ale	Federation	44
Highway	Elgoods	44
Home Brewed	Scottish & Newcastle	77
Home Luncheon Ale	Scottish & Newcastle	77
Home Stout	Scottish & Newcastle	77
Hook Ale	Hook Norton	57
Hoopers Ginger Beer	Bass	30
HXB	Gale's	46
Imperial Russian Stout	Courage	42
Imperial Stout	Samuel Smith	79
Ind Coope Light Ale	Carlsberg-Tetley	38
India Export Ale	Marston's	64
India Pale Ale	Harvey's	51
IPA	Bateman's	31
IPA	Brain's	35
IPA	Guernsey Brewery	49
IPA	Hanseatic	50
IPA	Randall's	68
Jackpot	Hook Norton	57
Jamaican Very Strong	Scottish & Newcastle	77
John Brown Ale	Hall & Woodhouse	50
John Courage	Courage	42
John Hop	Harvey's	51
John Smith's LA	Courage	42

Jorvic Lager	Mansfield	63
Jubilee Stout	Bass	29
Kaliber	Guinness	49
Kaltenberg Diat Pils	Whitbread	89
Kellerbrau	Charles Wells	87
Kingfisher Lager	Shepherd Neame	79
Kirin	Charles Wells	87
Kronenbourg 1664	Courage	42
Lager Beer	West Coast	88
LA	Randalls	68
LA Lager	Belhaven	33
Lamot	Bass	30
Landlord	Timothy Taylor	81
LCL Pils	Federation	44
Light Ale	Courage	42
Light Ale	Donnington	42
Light Ale	Gale's	46
Light Ale	Gibbs Mew	46
Light Ale	Lees	59
Light Ale	Marston's	64
Light Ale	Morland	64
Light Ale	Morrells	66
Light Ale	Shepherd Neame	79
Light Ale	Samuel Smith	79
Light Ale	Ushers	84
Light Ale	Wadworth's	84
Light Ale	Charles Wells	87
Light Ale	Whitbread	89
Light Ale	Young's	89
Light Pale Ale	Palmer's	67
Lion Roar	Tally Ho	81
London Pride	Fuller's	45
Low C	Marston's	65
Lowenbrau Pils	Carlsberg-Tetley	40
Lowenbrau Special Export	Carlsberg-Tetley	40
Lowes	Greene King	47
Mac's Brown	McMullen	61
McEwans 80/-	Scottish & Newcastle	77
McEwans 90/-	Scottish & Newcastle	77
McEwans Export	Scottish & Newcastle	77
McEwans Pale Ale	Scottish & Newcastle	77
Mackeson Stout	Whitbread	89
Maltsman Export	Carlsberg-Tetley	38
Maltsman Lager	Carlsberg-Tetley	38
Mansfield Bitterr	Mansfield	63
Mann's Original Brown Ale	Ushers	84
Marksman Lager	Mansfield	64
Mary Ann Brown Ale	Ann Street	27
Mary Ann Jubilee Pils	Ann Street	27
Mary Ann Pale Ale	Ann Street	27
Mary Ann Special	Ann Street	27
Masterbrew	Shepherd Neame	79
Master James Strong	Commercial Brewery	41
Maxim Light	Vaux	84
Merman Export	Caledonian	37
Mild	Aston Manor	27
Mild	Holden's	57
Mild	West Coast	88
Mild Ale	Banks's Hansons	28
Milk Stout	Guernsey Brewery	49
Mittlefrau Pils	West Coast	88
Molson Special Dry	Courage	42
Moonraker Brown Ale	Gibbs Mew	47
Moonraker Strong Ale	Lees	60

Naturally Conditioned Ginger Beer	West Coast	88
Nector	Rooster's	74
Newcastle Amber Ale	Scottish & Newcastle	77
Newcastle Brown Ale	Scottish & Newcastle	77
Newquay Steam Bitter	Whitbread	89
Newquay Steam Lager	Whitbread	89
Nicholson Strong Ale	Carlsberg-Tetley	40
No 1 Barley Wine	Bass	31
No 1 Pale Ale	McMullen	61
No 9	Bodicote	34
Norfolk Nips	Woodforde's	89
North Brink Porter	Elgoods	44
Nut Brown	Adnams	26
Nut Brown	Bateman's	31
Nut Brown	Gale's	46
Nut Brown	Harvey's	51
Nut Brown Ale	Palmer's	67
Nut Brown Ale	Samuel Smith	79
Oat Malt Stout	Maclays	61
Oatmeal Stout	Samuel Smith	79
Old Ale	Banks's Hansons	28
Old Ale	Hardington	51
Old Bob Strong Pale Ale	Ridley's	68
Old Brewery Strong Pale Ale	Samuel Smith	79
Old Dan	Thwaites	82
Old Episscopal	Ballards	27
Old Growler Special Porter	Nethergate	66
Old Hooky	Hook Norton	59
Old Jock	Broughton	36
Old Nick	Young's	89
Old Peculier	Scottish & Newcastle	77
Old Soporific Barley Wine	West Coast	88
Old Speckled Hen	Morland	64
Old Thumper	Ringwood	70
Old Timer	Wadworth's	84
Old Tom	Robinson's	73
Old Toss	Commercial Brewery	40
Olde Swine	Hog's Back	56
Original	Guinness	49
Original Porter	Shepherd Neame	79
Original VB	Randall's	67
Owd Roger	Marston's	64
Pale Ale	Belhaven	33
Pale Ale	Elgoods	44
Pale Ale	Fuller's	45
Pale Ale	Gibbs Mew	46
Pale Ale	Greene King	47
Pale Ale	Holt's	57
Pale Ale	Robinson's	73
Pale Ale	Samuel Smith	79
Pale Ale	Whitbread	89
Pedigree Imperial Pint	Marston's	64
Pelham Ale	Greene King	47
Pilgrims	Shepherd Neame	79
Poker Alice	Bass	30
Pony Ale	Guernsey Brewery	49
Porter	Burton Bridge	36
Porter	Harvey's	51
Premium Lager	Belhaven	33
Prince's Ale	St Austell	75
Prize Old Ale	Gale's	46
Pure Brewed Lager	Samuel Smith	79
Ram Rod	Young's	89
Raven Ale	Orkney	67
Red Stripe	Charles Wells	87

Reverend James Original Ale	Crown Buckley	42
Rhino	Carlsberg-Tetley	38
Ringwood Bitter	Ringwood	70
Robin Hood IPA	Scottish & Newcastle	77
Rooster's	Rooster's	74
Royal Oak	Eldridge Pope	43
St Andrews Ale	Belhaven	33
St Christopher	Carlsberg Tetley	40
St Edmund	Greene King	47
Sainsbury's Blackfriars Porter	Nethergate	66
Sainsbury's Bottle Conditioned Ale	Hanseatic	51
Sainsbury's Premium Ale	Batemans	31
Saint Andrews Ale	Belhaven	33
Santa's Toss 92	Commercial Brewery	41
Santa's Toss 93	Commercial Brewery	41
Satzenbrau Diat Pils	Guinness	49
Saxon Strong Ale	Ross	74
Scorpion Dry Lager	Vaux	84
Scotch Ale	Maclays	61
Scottish Lager	Belhaven	33
Scottish Oatmeal Stout	Broughton	36
Shandy	Banks's Hansons	28
Shandy	Lees	60
Shandy	Samuel Smith	79
Sixex	Holt's	57
Skol Extra Strength	Carlsberg-Tetley	40
Skol Lager	Carlsberg-Tetley	38
Skol Special Strength	Carlsberg-Tetley	40
Skullsplitter	Orkney	67
Smugglers Ale	St Austell	77
Solar Flare	Rising Sun	71
Special Ale	Federation	44
Special Bitter	Holden's	57
Special Brew	Carlsberg-Tetley	40
Special Export Lager	West Coast	88
Special Pale Ale	Timothy Taylor	81
Spitfire	Shepherd Neame	79
Stein Lager	Guernsey Brewery	49
Stella Artois	Whitbread	89
Stella Dry	Whitbread	89
Stout	Marston's	64
Stout	Randall's	68
Strong Export Bitter	Young's	89
Strong Golden Barley Wine	Samuel Smith	79
Strong Suffolk	Greene King	47
Stronghart	McMullen	63
Suffolk Strong Ale	Adnams	26
Sussex	King & Barnes	59
Swan Light	Carlsberg-Tetley	40
Sweetheart Stout	Bass	29
Sweet Sussex Stout	Harvey's	51
Taddy Brown Ale	Samuel Smith	79
Taddy Porter	Samuel Smith	79
Tall Ships IPA	Borve	35
Tally Ho!	Palmer's	67
Tarka's Tipple	Tally Ho	81
Tennents Dry	Bass	30
Tennents Lager	Bass	29
Tennents Super	Bass	31
Tesco Mild	Marston	64
Tesco Organic Beer Nature's Choice	Caledonian	38

Tesco Premium Ale	Caledonian	37
Tesco Traditional Premium Ale	Marston	64
Tetley Brown Ale	Carlsberg-Tetley	38
Tetley Special Pale Ale	Carlsberg-Tetley	38
Theakston Best Bitter	Scottish & Newcastle	77
Thomas Hardy's Ale	Eldridge Pope	43
Thomas Sykes Ale	Heritage	54
Three Hundreds Old Ale	Chiltern	40
Thurgia	Tally Ho	81
Tipsy Toad Ale	Star & Tipsy Toad	81
Toby Ale	Bass	29
Toby Brown	Bass	29
Toby Light	Bass	29
Tolly Brown Ale	Tolly Cobbold	82
Tolly Light Ale	Tolly Cobbold	82
Tolly Strong Ale	Tolly Cobbold	82
Tom Paine	Harvey's	51
Total Eclipse	Rising Sun	71
Traquair House Ale	Traquair House	82
Traditional Yorkshire Bitter	Black Sheep	34
Trent Bitter	Carlsberg Tetley	38
Triple Crown	Ushers	84
Tuborg Gold	Carlsberg-Tetley	38
Union Mild	Marston's	64
Union Street 200	Borve	35
Vassilenski's Black Russian	Hanseatic	51
Victorian Stout	Titanic	82
Victory Ale	Bateman's	31
Vintage Harvest Ale	Lees	60
Websters Green Label Pale Ale	Courage	42
Wheelwright	Robinson's	73
White Label	Whitbread	89
White Shield	Bass	30
Winter Welcome	Samuel Smith	79
Worth Best Bitter	Commercial Brewery	40
Worth Porter	Commercial Brewery	41
Wyvern	Gale's	46
XL	Holden's	57
XXXB Export Ale	Bateman's	31
Yakima Grande Pale Ale	West Coast	88
Yakima Grande Porter	West Coast	88
Yellow Mountain Beer	West Coast	88
Youngers Brown Ale	Scottish & Newcastle	77
Youngers Pale Ale	Scottish & Newcastle	77
Youngers No 3	Scottish & Newcastle	77